FINDING THE LADIES OF AVALON

FINDING
THE LADIES
OF AVALON

by

JAN KUŚMIREK

illustrations by
Stuart Littlejohn

In memory of Teddy Fearnhamm and
the blades she wrought which inspired
the journey, and Glennis Manns-
Morris who shared many journeys.

With thanks to Stuart Littlejohn for
the discussions, ideas and artwork
that brought the project to life, and
the many women of Avalon who have
manifested their goddess to me.

Thanks to Ranchor Prime for his
editing and completion of 'The Lake'.
To Shirley and her Angels for doing
all the things which make an author's
work easier and fragrant choices.

MERLIN

V

Published by Shimran
an imprint of Fitzrovia Press
42 Monington Road, Glastonbury BA6 8HF
www.fitzroviapress.co.uk

ISBN 978-0-9570722-2-0

printed and bound in Great Britain by Short Run Press
Exeter, EX2 7LW , England
typeset in Centaur 12.5 point on 15
printed on FSC papers:
Munken Premium Bookwove 80gsm

silk coated 130gsm

CONTENTS

Foreword   xi

I	A Journey to Avalon	I
2	Pathway to Understanding	II
3	Life in the Material World	27
4	The White Spring	37
5	Beckery	49
6	Merlin's Rant	65
7	The Coming of the Dragons	72
8	Swordplay	78
9	Dancing, Walking & Talking	85
10	The Meeting	93
11	Initiation in the Old Way	102
12	To Be a Water Maiden	113
13	Holy Ground	122
14	The Left-Hand Path	135

Afterword: Piran's Manuscript   145
Piran's Manuscript (the Thirteen Ladies)   aI

FOREWORD

Glastonbury is a small town in England with a heritage that draws thousands of visitors from around the world. It conjures up many images from its famous pop festival to its ancient ruined abbey and the oldest Christian site in Britain. The town is set like a jewel in the gentle, beautiful Somerset countryside, a land of willow, meadowsweet and still waters. Access to Glastonbury by road, rail or bus has never been the easiest yet visitors come in increasing numbers every year for a variety of good reasons.

As you enter town the roadside declares Glastonbury – the ancient Isle of Avalon. Ah Avalon! That ancient place of mystery and legend. A place of many names – the Isle of Apples, Ynis Witrin meaning the Island of Glass describing another world of magic. Is Glastonbury the Ancient Isle of Avalon? Are the mists that surround the Isle physical or ethereal, a reality or just a cloud in the mind? Where to start looking? These are important questions for the visitor, the seeker, the pilgrim and the tourist alike. Is it even possible to visit Avalon without ever going there in person?

Are you looking for Avalon? Do you visit Glastonbury and want to know what it is all about? In these pages you can start your voyage, for this is not a storybook or just a simple work of fiction: this is a guidebook. Like any journey it has a plan, the pleasure of travel and also trials and tribulations. To find Avalon through these pages you will have to think back deep inside your memory, to go back in time, into the future, to the very beginning of the end of the pathway.

You may need to visit the places mentioned in the guide for they are all there in the landscape of today. Find the old paths, feel the winds, listen and touch nature. Yes, you will have to dig a little, for both ancient and modern names are used. These pages will help you lay your imagination alongside realities, to see things differently in a world that has been, but is still present around and within us. Wherever we travel we leave something of ourselves behind when we have gone away. There are things in us we do not understand but which we can discover by going back. Something of us stays, there in the past, even if we have gone far away. When we journey to a place that has been part of our lives, we travel to ourselves and to those who have made us. Such is Avalon.

We begin the journey with lessons from history and geography which may seem dull and out of place beside more seemingly interesting tales. But to find something, as Merlin would say, you will have to seek, and know what you are looking for. Otherwise blind chance and luck come into play. In these pages are the thirteen treasures Merlin hid in Britain. You may find them, but only if you remove the fluff of romantic illusion about our predecessors, our ancestors who trod the path you seek. They sweated when they toiled, they itched when fleas bit, but they were also clean, enjoyed soap and water, appreciated good food and liked clothes. In truth their desires were little different to ours, but to survive they had to live closer to nature and the spirit world than today's people.

And what of the Lady of the Lake, Queen of Faerie? Here is a world that exists, which we enter at our peril, for here be dragons as well as fair folk. Those who were our ancestors had need to walk the spirit paths. There they found comfort in their souls, knowing they were surrounded by life beyond their own consciousness, and by the ancestors and spirits of their folk history. They saw them as we can also see them, but only if we let them be seen and heard. We do this by fully using our senses, by following our noses, by letting ourselves be overcome by what surrounds us. They are hidden from those who do not know how to look, hear, touch, taste or smell, for those arts have passed—but maybe not for you. For you are here.

So do as Merlin says…

Jan Kuśmirek
written under the mountains

2017

1

A Journey to Avalon

It all began very simply, in a shop on the High Street in Glastonbury. It was a bright sunny day and this particular store stood out, reflecting the happiness of the day with its bright yellow white and grey striped awnings and façade. Through the window I saw shelves loaded with potions and lotions for health, beauty and well-being. There it was beaming between two of my favourite bookshops, both icons of hippydom and alternative culture, both laden with books about Avalon and King Arthur. This golden store and its two neighbours were different to what I had expected in this town of eccentric, quirky, odd and sometimes tatty shops. It seemed out of place, with an air of magic, something intangible, an elegance of design that also contributed to the feeling of being 'different'. I saw this by watching the customers going in and out, passing through the sunny yellow and white doors from my vantage point across the road in my favourite and authentic café, the Blue Note, whilst sipping coffee and chilling, as my daughters would say. Dreadlocks and smart suits, tourists old and young, men and women. All seemed to find something there.

It was my kind of store. I bought some body oil that smelled of rose and patchouli, a pot of cream for sore feet and a booklet about the legend of the Lady of the Lake. I bought a postcard that was supposed to depict Merlin the Magician. I thought I would use it as a bookmark. The caste of Merlin's eye seemed to gleam at me from the image. Clever artist, I thought.

It was such a warm sunny day that I decided to sit in the abbey grounds under a tree away from the ruins and read a little. I passed a man I had seen in the shop. He had smiled at me whilst I had been browsing among the fragrances and staring at the striking painting of a woman standing in a sea of blue water. He had spoken to me about the Lady of the Lake and her powers in Avalon; he told me the painting depicted her, and in his opinion very well. He pointed out the hidden signs which could be found in the painting. All very interesting I had thought.

Now as I passed him on my way to the orchard he glanced at me with a brief smile. Odd, I thought, for his eyes were commanding like the ones on the postcard, as though he knew me. I smiled back and soon found a place in the shade beneath an apple tree. I settled down to read just like you at this moment. And then it happened, and it must be happening for you too, for you are reading the same page! You will find that where you go is now in your hands. The same voice in your head is the echo of what came to mine. He spoke, and speaks...

Hello, here you are then. Good. I am glad you arrived here on this page at last; I have been expecting you for a long time now. I know you are curious about me and that you feel you already know me—but you don't, you can be sure of that. For no one born of woman knows me. But I know you. No need to be nervous, this page does not bite. But do be a cat and be curious, really curious, for a cat looks and senses, tests and treads so very carefully until it knows. Curiosity kills the cat? Oh yes, but a cat has nine lives and nine is a magic number!

So as you are here at long last and have opened the book, I would very much like you to join with me just as in ancient times long ago;

come journey with me to another place right now. Not tomorrow but right now, for I am always impatient.

Do you remember? It is all there at the back of your mind. Your inner senses will respond to my tale whether you wish it or not. Time will fall away and you will see and remember things you cannot now imagine. For I am Merlin and I fly like the hawk over centuries, observing, advising and sometimes interfering, for I left my moulting cage when She of the Lake finally passed into the mists.

You see me now. Look inside yourself. I have put on my bright cloak of many colours, my many feathers that are iridescent in the sun and which let me shine as a jewel in the land. All those who have the gift know that colour is a key to being, as smell is to imagination. Even the lowly shaman knows this, with his beating drum and coloured cloak. I am Loki the trickster, the flame, the fire that flickers through the centuries. I am the playmaster as I was with Igrayne, Duchess of Cornwall, and some say I am Herlequin of many faces. You may think of me as Hermes if you will, or Veles of my favourite people, who came to this land by the hand of Rome. Do you dare trust me?

Already I can see you think me a bit of a mystery. Am I a magician, a wizard, a seer, or even, clever girl, a cunning man? I have always said, what is a mystery today, tomorrow will be a learned science. So am I real? That depends on what you perceive reality to be. If your work is in the science of what men call physics you could grasp at my nature. I said physics not psychic, but then a good psychic sees me anyway and has no need of physics.

I was always the alchemist ranging around Carcasonne and Saint Rémy with Michel de Nostredame. I lurked for a time in Krakow and Prague befriending Michael Sendivogius and the interesting Englishman John Dee who served the first Queen Elizabeth; those were the greatest of times when the retort birthed spirituous essences which expanded minds to feel the gods all around; strange brews and strange lights in dark rooms; sheer magic.

Ah, the Philosopher's Stone. How many times have I sent men on Quests looking for something which seems so in their grasp but just out of reach, like the Grail in Avalon, which place is your concern. Stone, cup, platter or condiment set—it was never a single entity my dear. It was no more than the summary of the thirteen treasures or hallows of Britain which I hid, or more properly, veiled. They are yet to be found in Avalon, for they are always here. Yet it never struck the Questors why it was that women did not quest. They had no need of this finding, for they had yet to be discovered, which is more than finding. Do you already see the riddle and the answer?

I have always dealt in riddles, signs and symbols, hence my love of alchemy, in your time named chemistry. There are always charlatans in alchemy and your chemistry. One such was Edward Kelley, John's friend. But it must be said Edward was very adept at commerce and far more so as a magician. He loved the gullible public who were prepared to believe in miraculous cures rather than actually do some work with the secret of nature.

Of course, before you ask, I helped Edward. He was my great friend and a trickster. It was his patron Rudolf number two, Holy Roman Emperor, and his wonderful Rose Castle who moved magic to a high status. That really was my interest for, through Edward, I led Rudolf a merry dance to all the new sciences and rewarded him with many carnal pleasures, which is my way. You may say he and I founded the Western Esotericism to which you subscribe, although you do not know it yet—or perhaps you do, for you are here on this page.

For nature is alive, as all good Druids know, and I hold some of that faith in me but not their propensity for blood. I have taught mankind to ponder life itself, the vital force that imprints a pulsating wave within all living things, be they animal, vegetable or mineral.

Some call it spirit, some energy; but call it as you wish, even the Gods and Goddesses live by it. Although it is without personality, we translate its power to our own will, or to those to whom we owe service in the spiritual realm.

What you feel is what I am. You may call me spirit, for I have no form except that which I wish, adopt or inhabit—and what you project. You may call me energy, which is less controversial in your age. For you to see me, to feel me, I manifest in those who have like minds or wish to work my ways. So my human form is mostly borrowed and I live within some like-minded men. They feel me as an old man looking out of their eyes at everything, and at you. So the person who has come to mind, and who you now feel is unexpected, is the one you joked with many times in the Galatea Café before it became another secret place. You called me Merlin. For that curious ancient place is where the Ladies are found—and that is your riddle. Today I might be in the Blue Note or lunching in the little cottage tea rooms, or just lounging in the Abbey grounds. Find me in the eyes.

How did this memory, your feeling of curiosity, come about?

At a time long ago, when the Sun ruled by the Great Rivers, before the great earthquake, before divine Atlantis fell, when the gods walked among men and the heroes and heroines of old were birthed, my goddess mother was seeded in the temple by he who gave the Blue Lotus life. She brought me forth there within the innermost chamber. It was a time of Great War among the gods which brought havoc to Mother Earth, who twisted, shook and writhed at the gods' behaviour. Those who fought to raise humans beyond servitude to the divine despot, the Oligarch whose name is hidden and must not be written, were trapped in this small universe. We brought gifts to mankind; fire and metalwork, labour and lust, music and free choice, chaos and rulership, and reliance upon the senses.

Our allies were the dragonkind. They were all but slaughtered when the great flood arose and extinguished their fire. A few remained in mountain caves, and kind men with souls akin became warlocks to help them serve as their good hearts once led them. But they were resentful at their loss in war. They drew their power from the sun and the glitter of pure gold which embodies the brightness and yellow of the eternal rays. These warlocks too, dazzled by the gold that holds men in thrall, became the Dragonlords of old. Balinor was the last and he in Arthur's time. I knew him well. When I, in the form of a changeling boy, displayed my insight, some said I was his son. But that denied my true eternal nature. The dragon pathways remain riven in the ground and you walk upon them, the ley lines, the old straight tracks.

We spirit demigods and fairy forms lost the battle, and so our power. We can no longer take human form as in the past, and so are confined to this world, above and below, and to what you see to be the heavens. But we have no access to that heaven above the heavens. So the gods, now invisible as dark matter, exist outside your human five senses. We cannot easily be seen or found. But those who have been touched by the gods in ancestry may know us. They can lend themselves and their forms to work our ways.

I entered this world at this cusp in time and action, in a sacred place hidden within the Owl Mountains, in the inner temple chamber full of sacred fragrant smoke or incense. My cot was shaped like a small willow boat, a cattle feeding trough or manger. I saw my kin in their glory but they faded through the smoke beyond my sight. I was abandoned in that dark four square temple vault. So I am of darkness.

They say I was found floating among the reeds by a kindly woman and she and her husband nurtured me until I was a young boy. They soon became aware of my nature and I helped them prosper into their old age until they passed over. My spirit mother came to me often in dreams. I saw her when I lit the sacred fragrant fires, I smelled her perfume as she took form through the smoke wraiths. She had been forced to flee the mountain cavern and hid far away in an island temple complex deep within the earth.

That is my tale, and why I can shapeshift more than most, for I was hidden, and still I can show myself but rarely. That is why I shift and change my garb, for I am hunted like the stag, my power to be brought down.

As for my foster parents, they are why I love humankind. I walk among the gods as the last of those who are close to humans; I am the only one who kept my form, by fluke being hidden from the despot ruler of the furthest heavens. But the final battle has yet to be fought. I will play my part as will the Great Queen, as will the Angel Princes of each race and people. It is our eternal purpose to unify, for the great despot knows he has to divide mankind by fear and superstition, by rule of right and wrong, by prejudice and by religious dogma. These do not unify, they only separate. Love is disguised as torture, peace as righteousness, equality as elitism, and respect for difference as heresy. But we shall be united in love and if need be in the final war at World End—unpredicted except by me. Then we shall win, as Arthur is the Once and Future King and my creation.

Satisfied with my origins? Is it truth or lie? Where are these places, for they are real? Perhaps you were bored, wishing to know more of Avalon and the Great Lady? So come with me to begin our sojourn. It does not matter how you see me or who you think I am, for I am a multi-faceted being whom you desire and lust for deep within your soul.

Yes, we will travel right now. We shall not travel by broomstick. That is such a silly idea, nor is there a high-speed version as in Harry Potter—how ridiculous! Though what fun if there were such a thing. The brush wasn't always at the back, you know, for it had its meaning as old engravings show. The brush should be at the front or the top (never leave a broom outside your house the wrong way up, brush down, for that will attract bad luck). Certainly Edward and Rudolf would have said the broom was a symbol of the Old Path, the phallic handle rising from the ground, and the brush... well, the rest I leave to your imagination.

Anyway let's get on. Let me unroll this carpet. Of course it's a magic carpet. How else do you think we could travel comfortably through space and time? No we have no need of a Police Box or a theme tune, and I know what you are alluding to. There is no need to be facetious. This is real, in what you call real time. It is happening now—which is why you are at this point of travel.

By the way, this carpet was given to me by Queen Zenobia of Palmyra before she led her revolution against the Roman Empire. See how shiny it is, made from the finest goat hair. Come, walk round it. See how the colour changes as the threads catch the light. One way it looks russet red, the other way pale pink. It is beautiful is it not, its geometry and the infills of the squares in oranges and blues, pink and sage, all dyes of vegetable origin? Life is in this carpet, given from the creatrix and her family, it has its own power to enchant.

Now stop vacillating. Come and lie down close to me, feel my body close to yours. Yes, it is suggestive, but it is what you want deep down. So now, decide to take this chance or not. The energy comes from inside you; it is not intellect that drives this adventure, it is you yielding to your senses, giving in to your hidden self. The outcome will depend upon which Lady chooses you. Have I not told you about the Ladies? I will, as the outcome of the carpet depends upon the choice, and it is not for you to make. Now come lie down and you will enter dream-time and move far away to another plane, to the Otherworld.

Close your eyes. Begin to sense your breath and feel the rhythm of your body. Feel the life-giving cool air pass through your nose and

8

into your being. Place your hands loosely on your abdomen. Feel the air passing in and out, in and out, slowly now, slower and slower. Feel your tummy rising and falling through your hands. This is your very breath of life, in and out. Let your legs part slightly and push down into your toes, slowly stretch out like a cat. Relax again and breathe in deeply, breathe right down into your body, slowly now in, and slowly out. Breathe in and out as you let your natural rhythm take you over. Push your hips lower and lower into the carpet, move your hands a little lower.

Can you hear the music? Do you hear music swirling, whirling inside your head. It is a whirling and fainting and fading, the feeling of falling from a great height. Ah, time slips and all seems so long ago.

Do you feel the warmth of the sun? Let your body sink to the carpet, the earth beneath. Yes, the ground is hard. But listen to me. Feel the ridges in the earth. Feel the tightness in your lower back; let it go, let it fall away. Do you remember when you were in the cot sleeping soundly? Breathe in and out, in and out, let the rhythm take you. Arch your back a little as heat rises from the depths at the base of your spine. Give in, yield to me. You are now in the Realm of Possibilities.

Look carefully at that riverbank, do you see the rushes sway in the warm breeze? They are so dry and white. They whisper words and names from the past. Can you see the brown-coloured water moving so slowly with no sound or ripple, just the green pondweed swaying with the movement? Take off your clothes. Naked now, walk slowly into the water, feeling it warmed from the sun, holding you more strongly as you push against it. As you walk deeper and deeper the water becomes colder, numbing, frightening, closing over you.

The waters draw you down into the dark. There is a hum from bees as you float again into the light, drawing you upward. You have become as the water, floating, still, and the sun is warmer now as you join the zephyrs of the air. People flash before you without disturbing you, just as when you sleep—and yes, that was your mother, but very young. A chanting ranter, accusing faces, water, gasping, drowning, then light and gulping air, then down again. A man with an orange sash shouting, then the warm bank and a gloved hand pulling you up. A clash of arms between Red and Gold, smoke and cracking muskets, stooks of corn, the smell of your father's sweat, a haystack and warm ale. Children old and young with ruddy faces, a steaming midden and the low of cattle.

'Oh Merlin now I can see a market and smell the sheep and goats, strange faces towering above, and noises. I am holding on to mother's kirtle, moving through the crowd, and there is a man singing. His song is of Roland, a knight of long ago.'

The music from his lute resonates within your ears and the tune lies hidden just beyond your grasp. You reach toward the singer and he smiles at you in his brightly-coloured clothes. You feel so happy in this glorious golden glow he creates around you. He looks just like...
   Hush my child; see the silver moon sail away through gilded clouds.

2

Pathway to Understanding

hud. Barley is shaken awake, disoriented, feeling dizzy. 'Oh Merlin what have you done? Where am I? I feel light headed, I feel sick. Did you have to jolt like that, could you not have landed softly?'

Merlin looks at Barley quizzically.

Don't rush, and stop gulping air like a stranded fish and take your time. I don't use the carpet that often, bit rusty you see, as it transports mortals and I travel beyond it. My pilot skills I admit are a bit off, so apologies, but we are here now so do quit moaning.

There, better now? Here let me pull you up. Feeling a bit more grounded now in the fresh air?

Barley manages a smile at Merlin's joke.

Isn't it a glorious day? You are standing on the highest point of the Quantock Hills. The Saxons called this place the Hill of the Strangers or the Ridge of the Welsh. For hereabouts in this time where we have come to, this land was called South Wales, the land of the West Britons, and over the sea to the horizon was naturally North Wales.

You wanted to know of Avalon. There is no better place to start from than here, high on this hill. See the great bowl of Avalon, natural cauldron of many waters. The Great Lady is of the Earth and see, she sits above so many waters. Look at the reflection in those lakes and rivers stretching south and east from the coast. It's not as your day is it?

To understand Avalon you must start with the land, as it was, as it is, for it is ever changing and moulds us all, and we live by its abundance and fertility. So my dear, I shall force you to look at history and geography—assuming you really want to understand, which is more than knowing.

Do not close the book, because you have to learn. There are no shortcuts or pathways that meander away from fact into fiction.

You felt you had been in Avalon before, in a previous incarnation. The thought occurred to you right there in Glastonbury in the twenty-first century, amongst the motor cars, trinkets from China and anti-quaries of the past, all mingling merrily. Don't you think that a little odd? What did you sense? Avalon, you will find, is a place where the four elements—earth, wind, fire and water—unite to form ordered nature or collide to make chaos. Out of this arises good or bad, from human views as mankind lacks the perspective of eternal time. Your human time is like dust that blows away. Time changes all.

From me, here, now in Avalon, you will learn to use your four senses of taste, touch, hearing and sight to discover the world another way, find other dimensions. And I will teach you to use the forgotten sense of smell. You will find the sixth sense to be real, for it will perceive the magnetism and electrons of the structure of her nature. Here in Avalon you will experience fire and water which when married in a cauldron yield from nature the fifth element, spirit, in which form the gods do dwell.

Never look for manmade constructions, for here nature is all around us. It is our temple. She does not dwell in handmade places. She needs not meeting halls when there are the groves and the trees that give the spirit of place. We seek her here.

Avalon is where the energy of time turns and returns in cyclical fashion. Chaos precedes order before it descends again to rebirth. Reincarnation, you should know, is in part about memory hidden deep within. So I am not going to argue about souls and suchlike, but I will stress that ancestral memory can indeed carry forward.

Do you realise, Barley, that there is not a place in the brain that just says 'memory'? Memory is not like a filing cabinet or a computer where we can just look something up and re-run the event. Most people think that is what happens, but it doesn't. Each time we have a memory we in effect recreate it, reimagine it, which is why memory fades and changes.

Do you not love music? How difficult it is to remember music, to hear a tune again in your head. Oft when you sing out the melody is wrong, the notes mingled with another tune and you cannot catch it. When music is written down and one can see it on the page, it does not become what it really is; it has to sing out from the hands of the musician. Until the molecules of air are vibrated to form waves of energy in different lengths, only then the music takes our minds and floods us with its emotion or movement. Even more difficult it is to recall the music of the wind and the trees mixed with the lowing of cattle or the rage of a stormy sea.

The Mousai of the Greek peoples are goddesses of music, song and dance, and the source of inspiration to poets, just as our Ladies of Avalon. The Ladies of the Lake whom you will meet and know well if you desire, are the embodiment of the spirit of knowledge, and they remember all things that have come to pass. Music attracts the spirits in another world. Humans communicate with music. But how can the spirits manifest except in you?

Fragrances jolt memory which is why when people talk about ghosts, they often mention strange smells preceding an apparition or haunted feeling. And dogs, with their exceptional sense of smell, hate haunted places! Smell is your lost sense, your untrained sense so devalued by mechanistic science, as a primitive sense we are never encouraged to use. But it is the sense that feels and touches what is beyond us in our hidden ancestral past. The nose peers into the fifth element to find the spirit of place or to seek the gods. Your nose is your hidden pathway to ultimate memory, as perfume is to the manifestation of the unseen.

The Romans spoke of incense and said of its smoke 'par fumum', meaning through the smoke you will see the gods. Not veiled as in smoke or mist but through the fragrance of the smell awakening your inner memory of the past, when the gods were visible and tangible. Hence our modern word perfume.

As he said this, Merlin sighed and tapped his nose, then continued.

Fragrance and incense have ever been the food of the gods. Fragrant smoke rises to the heavens and vibrates with our prayers to hold our thoughts, our music. Offer to the gods a favoured scent and they may well come to you, as may the little people. On the other hand some of the sprites, especially those of the household and the farm, emit sulphurous odours. So what pleases you may not please them! You are going to have to listen to and with your nose, Barley.

But let's get on with your Avalon. With knowledge gained by your living in what is now the future you abide in, you can look at what you see and what your senses tell you, then match your book learning and memory to what I show you. You may then truly begin to understand the nature of Avalon.

Knowledge is one thing and its use is another. The future is built upon the past, so never, never, underestimate the knowledge of what has gone before. Each present has its own arrogance but the wise look to what has gone before.

You whom I know as Barley Bright, like the sun-soaked corn, have journeyed with me to learn and recount our tale in future days.

The features of a land dictate its meaning and its people. Look around you. See, there are deer on the brow of the hill! They are the great red deer, but the smaller roe deer are here too. The purple heather comes from their grazing along with the wild ponies who have lived here since the time of the great cold. This is a land where the horned god dwells and where the deer draw the chariot of the goddess Flidais, she of the beautiful hair. She cares for the woods, its creatures, and the cattle of mankind. You do not see the spirits but can you not feel their presence in this place? You can see them in the colours of the leaves and flowers, the special brightness, the vibration in the air beyond the breeze.

Ah look, something has startled the grouse; see them jump into the air over there. Could be foxes or wild boar or even the wolves who come this way from the great moor where rises the river the Romans called Isca, meaning the river which abounds in fish. But let us hurry. These places are not always safe for the inexperienced, divorced-from-nature types found in the 21st century!

Come let us go higher up the hill toward the summit away from the scrub oak behind us. If anything is lurking, it will be in those woods. Come!

The pair stride on up the hill following a well-defined track where the winter rains have flowed and eroded the soil to expose the stones and rocks that make for tough walking. They strike off to one side, pushing through waist-high purple heather. In patches the ground is blackened by fire and the shorter heather regrowth makes walking easier.

You are breathless from the quick climb, Barley Bright. Out of condition? Take a breather for a moment. Isn't the countryside beautiful?

The sun is shining, the clouds fluffy high above and the breeze fresh from the West. Look here at the whortleberries, have some, see how my fingers are stained bright purple. What! You think they are tasteless? Well by your modern standards yes, but they are what we have here and they are free. These berries are what the red and black grouse feed upon, all sadly gone in your times.

I agree with you, the heather is beautiful, but I especially love the clouds of honey-smelling pollen, which rise like dust as we walk through the heather. And the hum of the bees on the wind is just the music of living nature, bland whortle indeed! Anyway, Barley Bright, wait till you taste our real wild strawberries, sweet and sour together, and in your day quite scarce. You just go to the stores for big watery, tasteless fruit and I can't think your blue berries are so very different to these here on the hill.

Look over there! Do you see the barrows, the burial mounds of the Bronze Age people? Yes, I mean those small hillocks.

Even back then, four thousand years before your time, traders came to this shore from Mycenae or Crete. They brought their own magic and power, and tales of the Labyrinth, tales of the Bee Queen and of the White Bull and the time before the Great Waters. And later of Troy, of Isis and, there on the island, Ishtar where her star can be seen to shine brightly in the waters. Here is the Summerland, the Otherworld beyond the gateway to the hidden chambers of the dark moist earth.

In these ancient burial chambers the people left great treasures. The grave goods they placed might be well-crafted battleaxes, metal daggers with elaborately decorated hilts, precious ornaments of gold and amber, and quantities of beakers. Among the golden cups, yet to be discovered in your time, are vessels shaped exactly like those from ancient Mycenae.

Believe me, King Arthur was not the first person to talk of holy cups and golden chalices. The holy cup is an ancient metaphor shared by many from time immemorial. It was not always as historians tell you, that people moved in mass migrations with fire and sword, one group displacing another, changing gods and ideas, making things right and wrong, black and white. Rather, change came from people trading. Trade and travel and the exchange of ideas, news, culture and goods have flourished in all times. The emblem of the sacred vessel, cup or bowl has been in these islands at the Edge of the World forever.

Now Barley, I want you to look around you carefully. Observe and take in more than just a glance; really see around you. We are on top of the world. Westward lie the Broom Hills and beyond them the Great Moor where the Isca River rises; even further, to your left, see the faint outline of the barren grey moor where the oak trees grow. In front is a line of hills which drops sharply away at the western end. Can you see the smoke trails rising? They come from settlements along the ridge and on the southern slope. This is where iron is smelted, now and from ancient times before the Romans came. Over on the other side is a bath house toward the old city of Caerwysc, which the Romans called Isca, your modern Exeter.

Now turn around and look toward the north and east. You can clearly see Wales over the sea. Wales is a name given by the Saxons, Wealas meaning foreigners or strangers. The Wales you see over the Severn Sea is the homeland of the Silures, a great and warlike British tribe. But as with everyone, the Roman luxuries and peace tamed them and now we call the place Gwent just as you do. Just outside your modern town of Street, along the road from Glaston, do you remember the village of Walton? The name means Welsh Town, or where the natives lived when the Saxons came.

In this time the native tribes are important to understand and relate to. Across this Severn Sea Gwent was always loyal to Arthur, the Great

Bear of the Britons, their war leader. It should not be so surprising because there, to your right where the land merges with the water in the far distance, was the Roman town of Isca Silurum which now you call Caerwent. The town and area ended up as a retirement home for Roman soldiers. The government handed out land to be farmed as soldiers finished service. As soldiers do, they married local girls. So from both the Britons and the Romans there has always been a military tradition in that area, which served Arthur well.

You see how many sails are on the sea? In your century you forget that in the past transport was mostly by boat. The rivers were the trade routes, just like your roads. True, the Romans had built roads. Once the Legions left, in 410 CE by your reckoning, without the mainte-nance of central government the roads gradually went to ruin and grass and scrub soon covered them.

Now please look carefully right down to where you can see this side of the Severn Sea, where the coasts curves in, with what appear to be a number of little inlets. Follow the main river to the right. That's it, you see? In the distance are ridges like fingers running toward the sea. You should know what those hills are called.

Yes, you are right, it is a plateau or upland moor. In our language here today it is called Mened, or in your day, with a bit of mispronunciation and Saxon thrown in, Mendip. They still do metalwork and mining up there. Lead and silver has been coming from your Mendip for centuries, and a long time before the Romans came. Iscalis we call it now. Used to be a bit of a rough area up there due to the lead and silver miners—always trouble, the miners. The Romans had an amphitheatre built there to keep them tame with a few games. If some of the slaves played up that's where they might have ended up, in the arena.

Don't sound so shocked. Of course there was slavery here, and still is. Always was, long before the Romans. The Celts were great slavers and head hunters too. Ah, I can see from your face that's a shock; not so romantic now are they, these artistic Celts! The worst were the Irish, always raiding for slaves and cattle. The Saxons too were always taking slaves. In the East, on the Saxon shore, slaving was their main business before they settled in Britain.

In Roman Britain slaves usually were granted freedom by their owners when they got older, say after thirty or forty year's servitude. All depended on the master. Apart from mining around here, slaves worked on the villas. No a villa wasn't a house like in your day at all. They were basically manor farm systems. Quite a few round here were not so bad, with a bit of luxury, central heating and mosaic floors; but most were rustic farmsteads often just run by the slaves. The landowners were absent in Rome or Londinium or even up the road at Aqua Sulis. But when the legions went the really absent masters basically handed over the keys and left the slaves to it, so by tacit agreement they became freemen. It's a sore point, for as the Pax Romana ended you can imagine it did not take long before the old tribal differences and jealousies surfaced. Then the big land grab began.

Petty princes made little kingdoms based on the old tribal system. Land disputes turned to minor then major civil wars. Roman Britain was finished, and the Island of the Mighty became a squabbling cauldron of greedy petty kingdoms.

It was easy for the Saxons in the East to hire their own people as mercenaries, then bring the family from over the sea, be awarded a bit of land by a local prince and bingo! Next a fight started with a neighbour who might be a Briton. Graffiti on the walls saying Saxon shites go home. And so, for security, a few more Saxon family members came from across the sea, and soon a community. Then before you knew it an area changed and became multicultural until the new group outnumbered the old. Then the laws changed and the original inhabitants become outcasts in their own land. That is what was happening in Arthur's day.

19

My role was to stabilise the tribes and get the Saxons civilised a bit. Less beer and more farming for both sides was my idea, and a gradual merging. I quite like the Saxons, stolid lot, quite loyal and less fickle than the Celts. Funny lot the Celts. You have the fiery Irish who love sad songs. And the Scots who are taking over Pictland, totally untrustworthy except when it comes to wealth, and so morose and feeling hard done by so always up for a quarrel with the neighbours. The Celts around here are independent-minded with a love for the mystic. The Saxons are getting a taste for Roman luxury and not as barbarous as they once were, so gradually moving west. Arthur gave us all a breathing space to calm down, assimilate and get on with life.

Anyway Barley, soon the East of England was settled or taken over by the pagan Angles, Saxons and Jutes. They worshipped the old gods for which some weekdays are now named: Tiw for Tuesday, Woden for Wednesday, Thunor for Thursday and Frigg for Friday.

Religion became a fault line not only between the newcomers but also within the Britons themselves. Christianity had grown fast within the Roman Empire after the Emperor Constantine converted. You already know that, but did you know that long before his so-called miraculous conversion, Christianity came to these parts, probably in the time of Tiberius Caesar and Jesus himself. News and ideas were brought by Middle Eastern traders. I know this to be true and there are all sorts of ways of proving it. For example, the daughter of Caractacus.

The story goes like this, as related by the Roman historian Tacitus. After the defeat of the Britons Caractacus the war leader fled to Northumbria, but the Queen of the Brigantes tribe, Cartimandua, handed him to the Romans. He was paraded in triumph through Rome, but as the Britons had given the Romans such a drubbing as never before, they had a certain respect for him and he was allowed to address the full Roman Senate. His oratory was so impressive that they allowed him his freedom and he lived on with his family in Rome with celebrity status.

The Jewish Christian missionary whom you call Paul, the sainted one, visited Rome about this time and got stuck there under house arrest. While there of course he became familiar with the local Christians, who were not at all popular. However, they were tolerated if they did not go around trying to convert people.

One such nominal Christian person was a centurion from Umbria serving in the elite Praetorian Guard. Now he had married the daughter of Caractacus who was reportedly a Christian when she arrived in Rome. In fact Paul, when writing to his acolyte Timothy, passed on good wishes from the local community including this centurion named Pudens and his wife Claudia, the said Christian daughter of the British King. Put simply she was a Christian when she arrived.

Now a lot of the tribes supporting Caractacus were from the Western parts of Britain, the Silures, the Ordovices and the Durotriges. Logic suggests that the legends surrounding the early Christian Community in Avalon or Glastonbury must be quite true. I was not here at the time to confirm the story, being in the North with Cartimandua the Great Queen of the Brigantes—which is another story—but there were certainly Christians in the West of Britain before they were in Rome.

What I can verify is that, when I got back from the North, a small meeting room made of wattle, you may call it a church, had been built. In my view it looked more like a synagogue with seats along the wall and a rostrum for someone to speak from. A bit later when the persecutions started, an altar was raised to the Queen of Heaven, whom they called Mary. Quite artful I thought, for who could gainsay such an act on the Island of the Great Mother. Mary, I later learned, could be a number of women or goddesses of that name.

I am not rambling, Barley, but just making sure that before we arrive you are clear as to what influences and conflicts you will find, so keep up. All these conflicts are in your heart and in your world today. Those who undertake the pilgrimage to Avalon in your day, to Glastonbury, will feel the same energies, still pulling and pushing for change and turning.

Let me bring you nearer to Arthur's time. Roman Britain, or at least its better class Romanised citizens, quickly adopted the Christian ways after the Emperor Constantine made Christianity the state religion. This state religion was not quite the same as taught by the people in the original wattle meeting room. It was a sort of pomp and ceremony affair that suited the rich.

Common people are not stupid. Country folk saw the success in war of the Saxon pagans, and kept to the earlier traditions of the Old Path. The gods and goddesses of hearth and home, field and harvest had always remained with the rural folk; those deities were still held dear by country folk, people of the land or pagans. The Latin word is 'paganus' which simply means rustic. It was a derogatory term if you were an upper class Roman citizen. The military class always held to the masculine mysteries of Mithras and the eternal sun. So religion was a defining line both in this civil war and in the invasion from the Germanic East.

I, Merlin the mage of this island, saw Avalon was central to the melding of the many traditions. I needed someone to bring peace, at least for a while. I needed some here to maintain the old truths and not the perverted way of Constantine. Bah! 'By this sign I conquer,' he had said while looking up to the solar disc, which in any man's eye forms a cross when looked at directly. Every soldier in the army already knew the power of Sol and Mithras. Politicians eh! Hence the rise of Arthur and the demise of the Lady of the Lake—stay with me for we shall come to Her.

No, you will have to wait. I want you to understand Avalon. Until you understand the land and the people, now and has been, you will just end up with an imagined La La land thought up by local charlatans.

Back to geography. Look in front of us. We see the great cauldron of Avalon. Two hundred square miles of Somerset. Those are the Polden Hills and along that ridge is a Roman road or what remains of it. That ridge divides the wetlands into two sections, to the south the really wild and sea windblown areas of the Zoylands drained by the sprawling, ever overflowing River Parret and its tributary rivers Tone and the changeling treacherous Carey, in your time tamed and drained. To the North perhaps a more cultivated area with your rivers Axe and Brue. This was the Great Salt Lake of ancient times when the sea came in as far as Glastonbury.

The Brue is nowadays the marker river for Glastonbury and is the cause for the great Lake and its marshes for when the tides rise it cannot do else but spill over the low land toward the sea. These rivers run below mean sea level! The road you see runs down to your Combwich which is just there, where more smoke is rising from the settlement. Can you make out some boats lying on the mud bank? See where the river bends? That's where the road takes you even in your day, because now at low tide you can ford the river. The road came up from Lindinis where the legions had a fort in the heart of the Durotriges tribal territory.

The rivers flow to the coast, where you see it is difficult to separate land from water or mud banks. The Brue and the Parret seem to join in that sea of reeds and rivulets. It is quite different here to your day; the sea comes in and out by whim of season and storm. The silt and land banks are too shallow to hold the sea back on the coast. It is quite possible to navigate low draft trading boats by poling into the heart of the moor certainly as far as Glastonbury when the tides are high. You could land close to where in your day Morrison's supermarket stands at the bottom of Wearyall Hill, as you call it (I know the store well as I have a Match and More card when I need things from the future). Wharves ran along toward Beckery.

Salt was panned there on the coast. Here were moneyed people on the coast and ridge road. Salt meant wealth and salt was equal to silver, so this was a wealthy place for those along the ridge or on that treacherous sea shore. Treacherous my dear because of mud, silt and quicksand and the high tides that flood the land, more so as the weather warmed since the colder times of Julius Caesars's invasion; the waters have grown ever higher since then. Nowadays to navigate the rivers you need a pilot from the marsh people and permission to enter the Sacred Isle—or risk an arrow.

Did you realise the tribe of the Durotriges gave their name to your county of Dorset? They fancied themselves as friends of the Romans from early on, especially once the big stronghold of Maia's Dun was taken. Lots of Christians in their parts. If you can't beat them, join them, seemed to be their principle. Their neighbours were the Dumnones—think Barley Bright, the letters mn easily turns to v. Yes you have it! Devon neighbours Dorset!

But Dumnonia in the West never got really integrated to Roman ways in the same way as South East Britain. They were more of a semi-autonomous area with all the benefits but less tax or policing from the legionaries; so quite a popular place to be if you had barbarian traits! Hence you don't find too many Roman villas Devon side, far more round here in the Summer Lands North and East of the river Brue. But still, the Romans managed to turn those Western Britons into good farmers instead of cattle raiders!

Barley is impatient to learn about the area where modern Glastonbury lay, not what was happening in Devon and Dorset. She interrupts Merlin's monologue.

'So what of all the people of that great green and blue plain stretching out below, the water and land, in your Bowl between the hills?'

Oh up there you mean, around Glastonbury? Yes, there were tribes thereabouts too. From the Mendip line, north into the hills you call Cotswold, or sheep hills, were the Dobunni. They went over to the Roman side from early on at the time of the invasion, when Claudius was emperor. The island however maintained its insularity. Folk on the island of Avalon have always had the blood of those before the Celts. I say Celts, but I want you think of tribes, because there was not a real race of Celts; there were tribes with different blood lines united only by need and power shifts of aristocracy. The blood of Troy lies strongly around these parts.

Now think about it. The great Iron Age tribes lie to the compass points of that vast flood plain below you. All around was an abundance of game, good farming, jobs, money, peace, towns and cities— but the wetlands and marshlands were different, these were the secret places of the marsh people. Why go to those secret places unless you were looking for the floating island where the souls of the dead are called in by the sacred hounds?

It is a place of water, where strangers are lost in the shifting reed beds; where the grey green mud sucks at one's feet and holds fast, pulling a person down until the mouth is full of grey mud and the breath is choked; a place without horizons, only sky above. You walk on ground that shakes and shudders beneath your feet, hastening on as the softness tells of treachery; then in an eye blink you are swimming in cold brown water. The tide turns and the rivers run fast without banks spilling freely as they will and rising to cover what looked like land. Tree roots of old alder, willow and hazel block your path as you wade knee-deep in stagnant swamp, where evil gases bubble from the black peat. It is a quiet place where every sound is magnified and echoed. You feel you are watched. It is a place of risk.

This is an old land and tells its story in left coppicing, abandoned trackways and mouldering villages. Times and seasons change. Now only the remnants of ancient people inhabit this place, along with their spirits, their old ways and gods. The Christians poled their barges upriver to found their community, at first hidden and secure in an already sacred place. That was before they began evangelising. The Romans left their mark with their roads and building but bypassed the communities that held strange faiths—although they acknowledged the presence of the Sulevi Mothers whom they thought of wrongly as Sulis.

The Celtic people hereabouts revered the waters of the earth, its springs and founts, lakes and rivers. So think Avalon and think waters of life, waters of death and the good moist earth.

Come let us fly down to my abode, where I keep myself to myself.

3

Life in the Material World

S o this is it, where I live and work, on this Mound—my humble home and next door my workshop. I like these square rooms or rectangles in the Roman way. You will find the Old People still favour their roundhouses but I am a moderniser, I suppose, and like the Christians I prefer four corners.

It's busy here on the Mound, which lies between the two worlds of the main island and the island of Witches. Over that way is the river Brue. You can see the landing stages for the boats and barges—I see all the comings and goings, all the traders, but less than before in these uncertain times.

Right now, in these changing days, we once again face the threat of Irish slavers, so a permanent lookout is kept downstream at an old Roman signal station. The Saxons too are not far away. The king of the West Saxons has conquered Sorbiodunum, which means the defeat of the Saxons at Baddan Byrig is forgotten: to them it is history. It was there on the ancient Ridgeway that Arthur stopped the invader until this time. But even so Arthur's legacy still means that the Saxons will not venture here for many years. For a while they will stay east of the old Roman Road they call Woden's Dyke. Their king, Cenwalh, yet to be born, will lead their advance and venture as far west as the Polden road and to us, for he unlike his father will not be a Christian.

27

After Arthur came the great plague when the land became a waste-land. Many of the surviving Britons fled across the sea to found a new smaller Britain. You know this land as Brittany in France.

No, dear Barley, I am not a fortune teller. Like you I am a seer, for we have already been on this path, although Cenwalh is yet to come for the people of now. You and I are one on this, looking forward and backward. It is a gift and privilege to access your ancestor's memories in dreamtime as you are doing.

The evening is coming in now. See the sun sinking in the west. Soon you will hear the chirping and croaking of frogs and toads; a lullaby to lilt you to sleep. Let me light the lamp as it is gloomy in here. Can you light the wick on the oil lamp? Just strike the flint against this steel. That's it, and again. See, not so difficult and once lit we can light the others.

Most of the roundhouses can't afford the oil I use, especially now the raids have cut the number of supply ships, so they mostly use rush lights. On this sedgeland we have rushes aplenty! The green outer skin is peeled off leaving the pith. These pith strips are then bunched and dried after which they are rolled in melted swine fat or mutton fat and if you are lucky a bit of beeswax to make them stiffer. They burn for about a half hour. Mostly light comes from the hearth or cooking fire anyway and working people follow the sun and season.

The Christian Monks here make candles from tallow and beeswax following the latest fashion, as oil is so pricey and in short supply; but they can be smoky and they stink. True they last a long time compared to rushlights. For My Lady of the Lake I have started to teach the novices the art of pleasing fragrant candles and rolling fragrant herbs to the tallow to give a better scent. But candles are still rare and are best used like incense in ritual and ceremony.

In the south where hemp is grown for ropemaking I have encouraged the seeds to be milled for oil, instead of getting it from olives, and some progress has been made in the distribution of this oil. And with the changing the people have had to explore new crops. No Barley, climate change is not new! It happens over millennia with or without man! Here it means we have famine in some parts and local political strife as it's easier to raid than grow.

'What about the thatches—aren't all these flames dangerous? For dry thatch goes up like a bonfire,' asks Barley.

You have put your finger on one of the biggest problems, Barley, and you are so right. This is where woodlore comes in. You can't afford to burn anything that sparks. Round here we have alder wood which burns quickly and doesn't throw heat, but we use a lot of it for track-ways and posts as it doesn't rot in water. We have applewood, for we are the Isle of Apples; it gives decent heat and a good smell but not much in the way of flame. Elm is good, as is ash, but elm lasts longer and is the final log as the nightkeeper—but it is a bugger to light. Cornish oak is good and found on the western side of the island; but we leave the old druid oak groves alone. They are found on the northern side and are said to be haunted by the souls of the sacrificed. Sometimes we use yew; a rare wood to burn but the hottest of all. We are ambivalent about yew as it is also a very sacred tree.

I burn logs because they are convenient to my lifestyle in the Roman way and I have silver money, but most hereabouts use peat or turf. Fires are generally kept alight year-round and you can burn turf, or sod, on open hearths or in the firepit. Turves are cut in summer and dried in stacks ready for winter. You will see them around here looking like big brown beehives. When work is done, a peat turf or even ashes are arranged to 'smother' the fire without extinguishing it, so it stays gently smouldering overnight. Then in the morning it's ready to be blown into life again. A fire going out is very frowned upon as the hearth fire is sacred—a family who let the fire go out would be derided, if not ostracised as bringers of bad luck.

Some of the houses have smokeholes to one side to avoid an updraft and a fierce drawing fire, but most do not. Inside this means the thatch is black with soot as the smoke seeps out. This is how the smoking is done from fish to ham; a simple preserving system. Peat smoke has a pungent 'peat-reek', and the smell gives a special flavour to fish or meat hanging from the roof or over the fireplace. Also, I might add, to clothes and people!

'What about real cooking?' Barley asks. 'How and what do people cook?'

All done on the fire, Barley; the cooking pot, the cauldron. The peat ashes themselves are extremely useful to the villagers in various ways for cooking. Hot peat ashes are excellent for roasting fish, even eggs, as well as any kind of cooking that requires a gentle long heat. A well-made heap of peat ashes can hold an iron pot quite steady, better than wood because a chain would be needed hanging from the rafters to hold the pot or kettle clear of the fire. Bread can be made on an iron griddle. There are plenty of ways to cook, but you better get used to porridge and believe me it will not taste like a packet from the super-market!

Cooking is not the problem, it is the weather, the harvest, the hunting and so on. The land round here and in the tribal territory grows garlic, onions, shallots, leeks, cabbages, peas, celery, turnips and radishes. I hope you like leeks for they are a staple here. We still have traded herbs like rosemary, thyme, bay, basil and savoury mint. In fact, a lot of these are now locally grown so we are quite civilised. You will see the swineherds and plenty of little pigs as well as chickens and guinea fowl.

Remember I told you how important water is? Well here we have an abundance of fresh water. In this we are very lucky. Most people do not have such clean secure supply and have to rely on good ale or small beer. We brew from spelt wheat here on the island but most tribes favour barley. We have a tavern over there on the island and I am known there, but many brew their own at home. Small beer or this mild ale is regarded as a sort of food here, being highly nutritious sometimes, with a consistency like porridge, I warned you about what porridge may mean, with just enough alcohol to act as a preservative. Good ale can be preserved with honey or if too sweet with bitter herbs.

Look around you Barley, freshwater and seawater a little way over there, so we eat a lot of fish and a lot of eels, shellfish, ducks and geese! We are not short of food till winter. We pray for a short winter but times are changing, getting colder.

Barley peers through the still open door, where a variety of moths are entering, drawn by the light.

'What are those twinkling lights right out there to the north over the water toward the reeds? They flicker and are gone after a moment. They look so pretty. Can we go and look at them, are they lanterns?'

That my dear is Will-o'-the-Wisp, or call them ghost lights. Some say they mark places where fairy gold is buried. But in truth it is the light of a bucca dhu or fairy spirit which delights in leading travellers to their doom. They must know you have come. Never follow such a light for the bucca dhu will keep moving their light to help you see the pathway they create through the sedge bogs, then suddenly they are gone and the traveller is stranded, lost and likely to be sucked into the slough of mire to meet the bucca dhu.

31

They belong to the fairy family who like to live beneath the ground in fairy mounds. This is a fairy mound upon which we stand and they are my good neighbours the bucca gwidden, a much friendlier tribe of little people. It always pays to keep the Fairy Faith, Barley, and stay on good terms with them. There are eight fairy families or clans. These are the ones some call goblins. Good William knew of them, hence he wrote of Puck in A Midsummer Night's Dream, that he might 'mislead night-wanderers, laughing at their harm...that Hobgoblin call you and sweet Puck.' I always leave milk outside my door for my resident hobgoblin.

Barley smiles at the thought of a fairy world.

'But surely these are just marsh gases, methane from rotting vegetation, and if your milk is gone in the morning it's due to nothing more than a hungry hedgehog.'

Oh Barley, how little you understand about magic, imagination and reality. You have to learn the nature of Avalon. Does not your science of Physics tell you of a world we cannot see or conceive, of energies beyond your senses; of living creatures that see what mankind cannot? Stay here awhile and you may yet see what you cannot. Your nose will let you see what your eyes cannot, for all nature has its perfume, a signature of being. And my dear, someone or something has to light the gas so whom might that be; spontaneous combustion? Or an energy you do not yet understand or know of? In science, you speak of dark matter or dark energy known to exist beyond our senses. I tell you that you have forgotten how to use your senses! You have a mind-set whereas the old people had sensation.

Ah, here is our food for supper. And this is Wenna. She looks after the house and is my cook.

Merlin speaks to his housekeeper.

Nid oes angen i bwa Wenna. Diolch i chi, efallai y Yiu adael i ni.

She does not speak English, and my magic is not strong enough when in this human form to engage your tongue to another, so English it has to be between us—unless you want to pick up some of the local language. I just told her she didn't have to bow to you and that she could go home now.

So this is what is called pottage and is really just a stew of vegetables and ah, this looks like some fish floating about. Just the one bowl for us to share. And here, this is good flat bread, still warm. Break it into pieces and you can use it like a spoon to soak up some liquid and bits, don't hesitate to use fingers, but mind, the pottage is hot.

Would you like some wine? I do have some, still made in Britain in the south east, but it is the Roman custom to add water and never to drink wine neat. Or you can try some ale. The Romans never got into ale. Okay then, ale for you, and this particular brew is flavoured with honey.

Whilst we eat I will tell you the way of sacred drinking. As you know, the goddesses accept as offerings, libations or drink offerings. There are a number of ceremonies or rituals where liquids are not only drunk but sprinkled, poured out or even used for sacred baths or ritual washing.

Usually honey mead is used on this island, especially for ecstatic ritual. Honey is so important here, and mead made from the honey of both wild and cultivated bees mixed with fermenting barley. Otherwise wine, ale, herbal brew or oil, water from sacred wells and springs and even blood are customary amongst some tribes. Special dedicated vessels are used such as glass jugs, clay beakers or cups, especially those with two handles. Here on this Island you will find the priestesses will sprinkle supplicants with the holy liquid from a glass vial using a wand or small brush, especially if it is a costly perfumed oil. Often these ritual practices are accompanied by fragrant incense or smoke.

Blood on an altar is a custom common to all the cultures I have seen on my travels in the world. Blood is seen by many as where life resides, and its spilling as death. The tribes, led by those manipulative and clever Druids, believed the soul resided in the head. Heads were taken in war by the tribes. Their practice was not common here, and their sacred groves hung with heads were not allowed in Avalon. This was more a place of the Goddess, and while human sacrifice might be an ultimate sacrificial end, strangulation and drowning were preferred by the priestesses hereabouts: a bloodless sacrifice where the hero was sent to the waters and hidden deep within the moist bogs. Don't look at me so aghast—you are here to explore and to open those places in your being where fear resides and where your capacity for reacting to the darkness of fear is tested against your inner soul.

The Druids were men. There were no Druidesses although there were shamankas, wild women. The Druids had no concept of cruelty, only of salvation, or if you like immortality through pain and sacrifice. Hence, you see, they were not averse to the ritual Christianity that came here from Rome. Such beliefs and practices had little in common with those of the first Jews who travelled here with their new teachings of equality and harmony, or with the idea that humankind is never equal in every talent but each talent has a value to be shared amongst the community. We may see this as a community of workers, but the lame and the sick were given credence for what they were, not their economic contribution. Such an idea did not go down well with the rich aristocracy or priesthood. But like a sponge the Oligarch is good at absorption—and distortion. Diversity is not the Oligarch's way, so much of Druid practice and even ritual clothing can be found echoing in the Roman and Orthodox Christian ways.

The Sea Peoples had brought with them their propensity for libation and drink offerings as a symbol of their life of giving, of ever giving service, a sacrifice poured out, not a single act of propitiation but a lifetime of reconciliation and association with divine living nature and with the unseen world of spirit forms. The offering was poured onto the image of the goddess. The liquid was poured on the feet as a symbol of submission or over the head as an anointing or symbol of dedication.

Another aspect of libation is the act of sharing an offering not to the gods above but within, a participation where we can look eye to eye over one vessel, share its holding and our saliva! It is they who taught the Old Peoples to use the honey mead and to keep the sacred serpents which we still do. It is they who taught the mystery of the labyrinth and the hive.

You see that wicker basket in the corner. In the autumn when the first frost comes, Wenna will bring in a grass snake to over winter. She will tell me it has the mark of the sun on its head so needs protection and that the snake is a messenger of the goddess. Snakes change their skin so have become a symbol of change and life after death. The snake forms spirals with its body, and resembles the umbilicus, the life-giving cord which connects new life with its source. But you have to remember they are symbols. Living creatures must not be confused with the entities and energies of the spirit world that we previously discussed. Snakes symbolise those feminine nature spirits you cannot see.

Oh, that rustling you hear? It's just the resident barn owl leaving home for the evening hunt. Nothing to worry about, and if you hear a hissing and screeching in the night don't worry, it will just be the owl. Barn owls do not go twit, twoo! And yes, you are right, they are white underneath and silent when flying, so common people in your own century mistake them for ghosts.

As the owl is flying I think it's time for bed. Come this way. There is your bed. The mattress is filled with goose feather so it's soft. Use

35

my cloak there as a blanket if needed. The smell is lanolin from the sheep's wool, because I use it as a water-resistant cloak.

Good night. May you see the Lady of your Dreams.

In the night the barn owl floats silently back to its rafter, then hisses and screeches into the darkness.

4

The White Spring

Barley wakes up feeling rested, at peace and well. She looks around at the ochre-coloured walls with frescoes of swallows and a white bull carrying off Europa, observes the scallop shell motifs that edge the architrave, and realises yesterday was not a dream.

'Good morning Merlin, I slept well. Isn't it a beautiful morning? The air is so clear. You are right, I can smell everything—cooking, animals, the thatch, the damp, the water in the pot, your cloak, you, and me even. It's so different. And the colours are so vivid and clear. It's all a little overwhelming.'

Ah, for the first time in your adult life you are using the senses you had as a child. This is how the world looked and felt when you first opened your eyes and the world was new! Later you were told to see things a certain way, taught that what you saw was not really there, that if you saw coloured lights or other-world creatures it was just your imagination. If you spoke to one of the little people you were told there was no one there, or even that you were in league with the devil. This is the way all humans lose their senses.

Anyone around you here can tell you that the rocks hold memory, and the stones, when laid out in sacred patterns, record our thoughts.

People have carved into these rocks and stones patterns and spirals like waves of the air, each touching the spirit world. Now your generation use quartz crystal with its vibration to record time, and rare earths to make your machines talk. You too have discovered wavelengths and colours beyond what you can see.

Everything is material matter, yet the Oligarch makes sure you think of your end as a nebulous heaven or as travelling to populate another planet, not as part of the present earth upon which we stand. You do not see Mother Earth, or your role as gardeners and friends of the soil, as children of the soil. You are made to think that tomorrow will be paradise, not that paradise can be here and now. You are told your body is no more than a machine, when really it is a vibration in time using the minerals of dust to take form. You pass from one generation to another but you forget who you are, except when you access your memories through ritual, dreamtime or potions and smokes. Your world is one of materialism with lip service to some spirit far away from earth. You are obsessed with right and wrong. Your priests are the scientists obsessed with their talk of dark matter and coinciding molecules; they do not see the greater reality. They are like explorers who cannot see the wood for the trees.

To know of Avalon you have to sharpen your senses, rely upon them and find your lost intuition.

Today you will meet Our Lady of the Heavenly Silver Wheel. She who is called by many names but here in time she is Arianhrod. Wenna has laid out some clothes for you. Jeans, tee shirt trainers will excite undue interest by the locals. Me turning up with yet another woman will not be such a surprise for my propensities are well known, but odd clothing attracts attention.

Here are some comfy slipper-like shoes, a tunic with a girdle, and a cloak with a brooch. I hope these help you adjust to Roman style. The brooch is copper and enamel, good Irish work. The tunic is a light heather purple colour from the lichens around here so will not be noticed too much.

The woman you will meet is like an oracle. She is a High Priestess who communes with the spirit world. As you will see, as a human she is a representative of the divine being who resides here, the Lady of the Lake herself who sits on many waters, mistress of the tides and springs. She organises her twelve attendants to follow the four seasons and declare the right time for planting and sowing, tupping and lambing. Her attendants are practical women, the backbone of rural society whose domain is from field to hearth. They are the healers, learned in herbcraft and able to use the power of the seasonal goddesses and spirits to whom they are dedicated. They are the Ladies of Avalon, the Ladies of the Lake, who with their maidens form the core of spiritual society. Most have the fairy blood of Lilith within them so they have second sight.

As there are four quarters of the year and four seasons merging and rotating, likewise at any one time there are three sacred sisters tending the sacred flame of the sun, for Arianhrod is the Lady of the Flame. Collectively these sacred sisters were known as the mothers, the Matres as the Romans called them. One mother is the central month of action, while the past and future mothers give her support and aid. This system, like nature, makes sure that as the seasons progress each of the twelvefold sisterhood in turn works to the benefit of the fertility of life, like a bride with two handmaidens. You might say three are always on sacred duty whilst nine are available for other duties. Hence we find nine Queens travelling with Arthur's body to Avalon to meet with the three Sulevi mothers, the triune Sulis, She of the sun flame in the water.

Between them they play politics with the local tribes and clan leaders, the petty kings and priests. All who rule know it is She who gives sovereignty over land, confirms authority and empowers by her embrace. She, the woman who leads them to her bed, personifies Arianhrod, ruler of Caer Sidi, the magical realm. Her home is the fortress of the Fairy Folk, which in real terms is Ynys Gwair over the sea. She is consort of the Moon God, who at best only reflects her glory, and by him rules the night. She is the deity of reincarnation, keeper of memories and dreamtimes. It is she who conveys the dead over water to their rest.

So come, I have arranged for you to meet Arianhrod at her shrine by her spring. She does not leave the Island of Witches often these days, as the Christians at the church are not to her taste and they dislike her latent powers. So it is a privilege for you that she has chosen to meet you by the Tor maze. Few go to the well these days except for festival.

Merlin and Barley squelch across the alder log track leading from the Mound toward the distant Tor. Black water and peat ooze through the logs, staining their shoes. They keep away from the buildings up ahead of them on the rising ground and head to where Barley knows will be the old chain gate of Glastonbury. Reaching a stream they follow it upward through apple trees festooned with mistletoe.

'I suppose the Druids used all this mistletoe,' she calls out to Merlin.

Not so Barley, they used the mistletoe only from oak, none else would do. Mistletoe does not usually take too well on oak hence the scarcity value of the golden bough.

The ground rises all the time. Barley realises they are following what she knows would become Bere Lane. Soon they come to a trackway leading east which Merlin explains was an old Roman road. Sometimes you can feel the cobbles beneath the covering of grass, mud and moss. They pass lines of straw beehives, keeping well away from them so as not to disturb the bee people.

Look there Barley, see how the waters shine in the sun. See the Lake - her land. At night you will see the silver wheel in the sky, the turning polar stars that never set.

It is true, as they rise up the hill the nature of Avalon emerges; floating like an island in a sea of mirrors. The reeds, so close and dense when you are amongst them, become just intervals, blurring the reflections and exaggerating a mirage-like scene. As the shining from the sky intensifies, the horizon between sky and water is lost and she becomes dizzy, intoxicated by her own reaction to this clarity of vision.

Merlin gives her his hand, and despite Barley's own exertions his hand is warm to touch. A soft warmth that is immediately reassuring yet oddly exciting as the warmth spreads along her arm.

This is where I leave you, Barley. See the track which leads into that grove of yew trees running uphill on your left, where the dark yew fades into the wild sour apples and the stunted Cornish oaks hanging with grey lichen? Before that line the path will branch left and right. You take the path to the right. When you reach a pool, wait until she shows herself to you. You are on your own now. Go.

Barley walked on, leaving Merlin behind. Soon the track divided, the one leading to the left clearly more frequented. Brambles and stinging nettles obscured the right-hand track, which was overhung by guelder rose, the berries soft and voluptuous, matched by elders with their blue-black hanging clusters. Suddenly the trees and shrubs opened to a glade, in which a pool lay beneath a rock face down which water trickled. A stream emerged from small caverns in the rock face to run into the pool. Further up water spilled from a larger opening.

And now Barley speaks to you...

'I say water, for yes, it was clear and sparkling, bubbling and murmuring as water does, until it came to the pool which seemed still and dark. From there it ran in a tumbling stream. I saw something dart, but it flitted so quickly from sight I guessed it to be a wren or some such, yet I had a feeling it had been the palest blue. A trick of the light perhaps, or just my imagination.

41

'What was clear was the magic of the place, for all the twigs and leaves around the dripping waters or streamlets were coated white. The water trails on the rockface were white, glistening as the sun caught the wet rock. At the pool edge were outgrowths of white lime formed like frozen bubbles. Looking carefully, I saw ancient offerings now turned to rock, amulets and ribbons all solid white. An overhanging hawthorn dipped its branches to the glade and some old clouties hanging from its branchlets had become calcined. Yet a few more brightly coloured wool and cloth strips told me this healing pool was still used by the faithful.

'You can see today in the 21st century what remains of this beautiful valley. Mankind has ravaged the place but caring folk still tend the waters, and the spirits and sense of place remain.

'This White Spring was evidently the place I was to meet the Lady of the Silver Wheel. The sky reflected in the Great Lake told me this, as did the Tor reflected in this pool. Here was the place of the White Goddess. I felt a presence, an imprint of something else. I also had the disturbing feeling of being watched, a feeling of excitement, anticipation, almost flirtation as though a man were present.'

Barley waited as the sun grew higher. Unknown to her, she was being watched.

Yes it is I, Merlin, who was watching her. I had shape-shifted to an owl, temporarily leaving my human form lifetimes far away in the future lying asleep in my bed. Sometimes I think that a time-travelling police box would be preferable to the energy I use in my shifting appearances. I hid amongst the leaves, for I had no desire to be mobbed by daytime birds. Being pecked and heckled was not on my agenda.

As humans are wont to do, Barley quickly got bored. I watched her

42

examine how the water had turned the twigs and rocks to creamy white. The covering was not slimy but hard and crystalline. She clambered up the wet rocks toward the small cave opening, but having slipped a couple of times and got one shoe wet, she gave up. What appeared to be a pretty moss bank she found to be damp and wet when sat upon.

Pulling herself onto a rock beside the glen, she looked out past the bushes to see surrounding the island a great lake shimmering in the sun. Looking north, she saw a sward of green mixed with water stretching to the horizon where it met the sky. She knew the sea must lie out there, with Burrow Mump to the right. She sat down carefully upon the rock, letting her feet dangle and staring dismally around the glade. Once she slid down and vigorously attacked a clump of meadowsweet with a stick. I assume she thought it was stinging nettles. She pulled at some herb-Robert and lousewort, becoming interested in the pale pink flowerets. Eventually she found a drier spot and lay back with her hands behind her head, staring upward at the early autumn sky replete with fluffy clouds. Well, I thought, at least that's a start toward stillness.

The air was warm and filled with the drone of insects. Some landed on her to be brushed away. She looked for her watch which of course was not there being left at The Mound along with her modern dress. She did not notice the shift of shadow which would have told the hour at least. She dozed, which is a human's answer to stillness and quiet. A late butterfly landed lightly on her hair, his wings open to draw in the energy of the sun. The little piskie of the place emerged briefly, palest flickering blue, like the wisp. You could see his pointed ears and little hat quite plainly before he faded. He knew I was there watching and had no power over me. I thought if she were awake now she would see a flash of blue and think kingfisher, even though this was not the right habitat for such a bird.

When she did finally wake, of course she was stiff. The sun had moved and the glade was more shadowed. Evidently hungry, she tried a few of the early blackberries from the brambles but they were hard and unripe. So she pirouetted a few times, did a few Swedish exercise moves, then flounced back to the rock saying, 'Come on Merlin, where the hell are you? Is this one of your tricks? I've been here all day bored out of my mind and hungry. F**k you Merlin, why am I here at all? I'm off. Do you hear me? I am sure you are watching me you old sod.'

This of course was the way women spoke in her time, I think because they thought equality meant that it was their right to be as vulgar and foul-mouthed as the most common man.

So she gathered up her tunic and set off the way she had come.

She took no more than ten or so steps before she quite literally stopped in her tracks. Coming from the opposite direction, blocking her way, stood a man naked except for a loincloth. She gasped and stood frozen. He was coated from top to toe, including the cloth hanging between his legs, in greyish white clay. Even his long hair hung with clay. His face and forehead were pitch black apart from a small crescent of white that stood in contrast on his brow. Across his waist he held a half-drawn short hunting bow. It was aimed at her.

In his language he told her to go back. Waving the bow and arrow gently back up the path. She could not understand the words, but his meaning was clear. Slowly she backed up watching him. Just as slowly he retreated, till both lost sight of each other.

She was now clearly frightened. She crouched behind the rock not caring whether the ground was wet or not, clutching her knees to her chest. Darkness stole over the grove and the sounds of night began. I gave the cry of a tawny owl and another owl answered. It was time.

All of a sudden there was my Lady, seated in a niche forming a ledge on the other side of the pool. For all the world she looked as though she sat upon a throne, the flat rocks a backdrop of shining pale light. She was lightly veiled, but as I watched she lifted her veil and stared at me. Swiftly I came back to human form and bowed before her.

'You chose my totem owl,' she purred. 'How sweet of you.'

She wore a red silken gown that swept from her throne-like seat in great folds. Her hair was braided with red but over all she wore the whitest silver cloak, threaded to catch the moonlight. She wore the golden torc of authority, and her aquiline face, painted grey, bore the blue mark of Three.

'You are scrutinising me, Merlin. True, I have grown older. I do not think another will rise from the sisterhood to follow me. They turn to a different, broader red path now. The narrow labyrinth spiral is replaced by a broad way. The meaning of the sacred cycle of nature is lost except to a few. Man-made laws prevail where once was only Nature's lore. I wonder sometimes if She who comes through me would better be served now by the Saxons with their northern pantheon. But no matter, time will tell. I must let her speak through me now.'

She cast her eyes down and entered a trance-like meditation. Her knees parted and her hands rested on them. A quiet low voice emanated from her closed mouth.

She called out to Barley who was still crouching behind her rock, partly cowed and afraid. Barley was disconcerted by my behaviour as a talking owl, my return to human form, and now my apparent lack of concern for her state. She was overawed by what she saw.

'Come woman, come here to me,' called the Lady. 'Have you learned the lesson of the day? The evening star is now bright. Have you discerned something of value? I am Spirit Goddess. I do not come when humans demand or call. You may dance your circles, light your fires, you may cut and show blood, you may tempt me with fragrance and smoke, you may bring me offerings and libation, but I am the

Goddess. You can serve me only when you understand my will. Only then will I lend you my power for my own purpose. Then you will see me clearly. I have made you wait to teach you patience, waiting for the moment. Timing is all. You have experienced fear so that you may know your limitations, and my limits, for you should fear me too. Did you seek me? I think not. Did you expect me, demand my coming? I know so. Now you must consider yourself a humble willing servant, a supplicant.

'I am Mystery and I am at the centre of all effects,' the Lady continued. 'I rule the sisters four times three. I have no time, for I am time. I look both ways, past and future, but the moment to be seized is only now. I cannot be changed, but I change thee. You need light to recognise me but you must sense me without light if you wish to know me.

'As you request, I will show you the meaning of Avalon, although the purpose is evident in any butterfly or dragonfly. You must find your ancestors within you then let them be manifest in your being, for they are there in your Lilith blood. Capture their experiences, access their memory and you will be a new being.'

The Lady turned to me. I had just returned to owl form and was peering down from a branch of the hawthorn tree.

'And you, Loki, Lugh, Prometheus, whatever you call yourself these days, have you been walking about in my Earth?' she cackled. 'Have you been playing with fire again? Which of my sisters have you been humping lately? I will tame you however slippery you are.'

'Why thank you, My Lady,' I answered. 'As ever I look forward to being stroked or healed. All I can gently and politely say in my defence is that it was Sekhmet's lions who were tamed at Leontopolis, and I do love pussy... cats, I mean. So with cultural reference, since you ask, I am rather into Kupala at the moment.' I smirked as owls can, for I knew this was a really clever retort.

'Always the clever one, my little lesser god, and always talking of Arthur's ancient people. They will be the undoing of your world,' she sighed, and returned her attention to Barley.

'Listen to him, Barley. He will tell you of the waters and the grail and of my sisters, and He who resides here in this mount. Listen and learn, but also discern between truth and conjecture, and see the meaning of words and places you do not understand. He was here before these Celtic tribes. He was here when giants walked this land, or so they appeared to the small people with their darts. He saw the coming of Brutus the Trojan, and he knows why this land is called Albion. He was here when the Sea Peoples came with the swallows bringing their white cattle. It was he who taught Tubal to be the first artificer in copper, brass and iron. Tubal was a descendant of the Dragon Queen named Lilith. He came from the wild lands and settled here, for he needed white tin for his favoured dragon people with their magic seals.' She looked at the sacred pool.

'This is the Moon Spring. Here the light of the sun is reflected back to shine in the pools like stars. The great Moon God, he of most ancient times, sprinkles his white seed over all who come here. He is husband of all women. Men are drawn here by his power, for here is what all men seek. He is the measure of all time. When in darkness he hides for three days, his descent and resurrection bind many cultures past and future. For we live by light, not by darkness. Yet our women's magical power is of the darkness. It is what men fear. I am the great Moon God's familiar spirit. Like the serpent I shed my skin to live in whom I choose; for I too am wisdom.' The Lady paused.

'Let Merlin be your guide, but never your mentor—that is the role of my women servants.'

Her quiet calm voice stopped. The glade was silent except for their gentle breathing. The oracle Arianhrod stirred and opened her eyes.

'Is it done? Has She spoken?'

'It is done, my Lady of the Silver Wheel,' said I. 'Thank you. I know how draining such an event can be.' Shedding my owl shape, I stood once more as I had been.

I turned with Barley and walked away toward the Mound. I produced an electric torch muttering an apology, 'Sometimes the future has useful things to offer. I have no wish to break my neck or fall in a bog.'

5

Beckery

next morning I woke late. Yesterday felt like a dream, an incongruous set of unrelated and unreal events. But my hunger was real and breakfast beckoned. I didn't recall eating anything at all on the previous day. Everything in my memory was too brightly lit. My burning question was, had I really seen that woman at the silver well? And had I seen that strange, threatening white-painted warrior?

As I collected my breakfast from the communal pot I saw Merlin, busy sorting out his coloured powdered rocks. He collected rare earth colours for Piran, the artist at the Abbey who was responsible for illuminating copies of the gospels and other holy books. Piran was a Cornish monk, so not quite kosher, as Merlin described him later.

'Sort of a pagan Christian, Barley, more artist than monk and I think ahead of his time in style. He has an eye for the ladies, so watch your step there, young woman.'

A sudden crack in my mouth broke my reverie. Something in the porridge had hit a tooth. Sifting through the mush with my tongue I located the offending bit. I peered at the piece of grit I found, hoping it wouldn't be a bit of tooth or filling. It wasn't white, or that grey-black of an aged filling; it was truly a piece of grit from the mill. Merlin had warned me to be careful of chewing away without thought. I rolled the piece of grit between my fingers, thought about the crunch it had made and my pang of fright about tooth or filling.

'No,' I said out loud, 'this is no dream.'

'No it is not a dream,' echoed Merlin as he came through the door back from his daily walk, having made his round of observation points that a later world would call weather stations. He watched the clouds and tasted the wind, smelled the air for what it held, looked at flowers and leaves for what they could say of the next few hours, let his skin tell the humidity of the air and touched the good earth to feel its temperature.

'Today will be fine, with a blue sky and a light breeze, a lovely Indian summer day,' he announced. 'Can you ride? Well you are going to have to learn fast, as the ponies will be here shortly. Exmoors you would call them. Not so big, but sturdy. They have been on the great moor for thousands of years. One of the Meare Maidens, Daughters of the Water, will collect us.

'And before you ask me,' added Merlin, 'meare is an old word for lake or sea. So there you have it: mermaids, Daughters of Water baptised to the service of the Lady of the Lake. The Meare Maidens help teach the young the ways of herbcraft and instil in them the cult of the Well Damsels, the ones who can divine where water lies beneath the ground.'

Merlin's cat, named Enya, rubbed against my leg purring happily. Enya meant nut kernel, after the honey-colour of her coat. Merlin was proud of his prize cat, who he described as sensible and cautious. As a kitten, she had travelled all the way from Egypt via Rome. She was well fed, and a good ratter I was told. I had not expected to find a cat or any other pet, but Wenna kept what I would have called a small greyhound. Merlin said the Romans had introduced them. She was part pet and part hunting dog. I was beginning to realise I had only thought about the mysticism and romance of the times, not their reality, their sweat and toil.

I noticed the pungent ammonia smell of the ponies before I saw them. I watched the girl riding the lead pony as she approached the Mound, splashing through the low brown water and pushing aside the straw coloured reeds. Her hair was the colour of the reeds and her legs were bare against the red blanket serving as a saddle and the dark brown of her pony. Her pace picked up as the pony lurched upward on to drier land, and I saw there were two more ponies in tow. She waved at Merlin and called out to him in the unintelligible language of the place.

He must have read my thoughts.

'Ah, so you have found a riddle,' Merlin laughed. 'The Lady spoke with you last evening and you heard and understood every word—but Wenna and Orla, the girl on the pony, speak the local dialect. So now you know your interchange with the Lady was supernatural in the true sense. She was a real woman who allowed the spirit to use her and speak through her. We may not take human form as ourselves but we are able to speak with humans in any language. Perhaps this is an over-sight by the despot Oligarch who wants to separate us from the humanity we love and desire to be with.'

The ponies arrived puffing and snorting as ponies do. Their oat-meal-coloured muzzles scented the air as they swept backward and forward searching every sound. Their big eyes stared at me without expression but their nostrils kept opening and closing like the gills of a fish. Evidently their brains were working overtime on the smells my futuristic body carried with me. Wenna through Merlin had already told me that I smelled of cheese, which I had not taken as a compli-ment. He told me as my diet became more natural this scent of decay would reduce. Decay indeed; I told him we lived longer and better than now.

I touched the first pony's muzzle and he instantly bobbed his head away. I am always surprised how hard the head of a horse and pony is yet how soft the lower lip. Orla called down, which Merlin told me was her saying not to dab at the pony but be direct and firm. Orla was pleasant enough to look at with brown eyes and a firm figure. She appeared half my age, so I thought she was twenty-four or so. She spoke, waving to me to get on the second horse. Merlin interpreted her words.

'My Lady Enid, Lady of Joy, virtuous and faithful, invites you to the Island of Women which the Christians call the Island of Witches. She of the Silver Wheel commands the Ladies of the Lake to bring you to understand our ways. Please mount and follow me. Our friend the Magician Merlin will accompany you until the Ladies gain your trust. Come!'

Now came the moment I had been waiting for. A rush of thoughts spun through my mind. Yesterday was real. The brightness, the silvery whiteness, the white water, the moon pool, the woman: all were indeed real, not illusions or dreams. They were as real as the rough hair and solidity of this pony. As real as the now obvious problem of to how to get on this horse. I realised that yesterday had been like jet lag, the sense of not belonging in time that comes with long haul flights. Astral travel, or whatever you call this, was indeed a physical drain. Merlin the gentleman came to my rescue.

'Hitch up your tunic, show a thigh, come on. Now when I cup my hands you put your right foot into the cup and grab the horse's main and at the same time heave yourself up and throw your other leg over the back of the pony. I did as I was told but was not expecting that Merlin would thrust me upward with such force. I felt for a second I would land on the other side. Instead I found myself with my face buried in the pony's rough and none too clean mane, but at least astride the animal. Pulling myself upright I saw that the ground looked a long way down.

And now for a moment I could take pleasure in the thought of Lady Enid. I had recognised the name instantly. The tale of Geraint and Enid in Camelot. At last I was to fathom the Mysteries of Avalon, or as Wenna called the Island in her language, Ynis Witrin, the Glassy Island.

The ponies began walking and quickly I got used to the swaying motion as we pushed our way through the reeds. The reeds were so high I lost my sense of direction. At one point we lurched down into water and crossed the murky river—or was it a tributary, I wondered. It was narrower than I had thought and too small for anything except punts. The silence was amazing, for as soon as we entered the reeds the sounds of the town and the wharves faded. There was a boom from a bittern, that throbbing deep call, yet I saw nothing but reeds. A dabchick hastened and splashed away. The horses snorted and with the sun on the back of my neck I gathered we had swung to the north and were now heading to the East of the island. I had expected to go to the pilgrim route skirting Wearyall Hill, not this way at all. Ahead above the reeds I could glimpse what looked like a wooden gateway, some carved uprights and a large crossbeam.

The reeds parted and the ponies pulled out of the water onto dry land immediately in front of the curiously carved posts and beam. The ponies paused and began cropping at the grass and sedge. I looked closely at the curiously carved wooden 'gateway' for I could think of no other phrase to explain the monument. Elongated figures of naked men and women entwined and embraced upward to the cross beam; entangled with them seemed to be a serpent which twisted and turned around the bodies. At the cross beam the bodies turned and slid across the beam from side to side in various stages of copulation. In the centre was a circle with a cross transposed. I had many times seen similar designs on Celtic crosses in Cornwall.'

'The Solar disc with the solstice and equinoxes marked out,' Merlin spoke from behind me. 'It's a spirit gate, an energy line or ley line if you prefer. You will find them from time to time in the countryside if the peoples have kept to the Old Path which was before the Celts and Romans. It marks the entrance to sacred ground. In your day you can still see some in Japan.'

The wood was weathered and grey with an aura that spoke of a lack of care. The girl made some gesture with her outstretched left arm and the ponies moved on as though obeying her signal. Straight ahead I saw some roundhouses. The thatch snugly running down almost to the ground looked so cosy. Although smoke rose through the thatch there was no sound and no sign of anyone, man or beast. Even the insects seemed quiet. To the side was a line of beehives, but no bees. I felt as though even the bee people were watching, hidden. I felt a presence, but saw no sign of anyone looking from the doorways.

Orla slid from her pony and waved me down. I slid off the pony and found that even in that short distance my body had found muscles I had not known were part of me.

Orla beckoned me to follow her to where a ladder seemed to stick straight out of the ground. When I got there I saw it was a pole ladder leading downward through a trap door into some sort of chamber.

'Should I go down?' I asked, though I knew Orla wouldn't understand a word.

Orla answered in her lilting tongue and gestured that I should. I turned doubtfully to Merlin.

'Well you wanted to come so down you go,' he said grinning.

Reluctantly, while Orla held the top of the ladder, I carefully climbed down one step at a time. As I reached the bottom I looked up at the entrance, seeing the sky above. Orla pulled the ladder upward, and before I had time to collect my thoughts I heard a trap door above thud down. For a moment I was in complete darkness, and I began to panic.

'Let me out,' I shouted. 'Help! Merlin, what the f—k's going on, damn you, get me out of here.'

Then a woman's voice spoke. I became conscious of her voice before I heard it, if you know what I mean.

'Just breathe slowly and look around you,' said the voice, 'Take your time, there is nothing to fear here.' The voice spoke in English but with an almost Welsh lilt.

As my eyes became accustomed to the darkness I realised I was not in total darkness. Th space was dimly lit.

I was in a circular underground chamber with a bench of grey lias stone running around the circle of the low vault. An elderly woman sat over to my right. She seemed to have a shrouded attendant on either side of her but these were indistinct in my vision. We stared at each other for a moment in silence. Silence I always find unnerving and I wanted to fill it.

'Hello, my name is Barley.'

Silence and no reply. Try again, I thought.

'I never expected to end up in an underground pit, but it's nice and cool down here. What's it for, this place?' I knew my words sounded inane, but what else to do?

'My dear, you talk too much. Instead of asking silly questions look around you. Listen to the silence. Observe using all your senses: feel, see, smell and listen to your inner self. When you are ready I will talk and you will listen.'

My reaction was at first rather contrary. After all, she hadn't been thrust down a hole into the dark. The old crone at least knew where she was. So why should I be bossed around?

Looking round I realised the 'pit' as I had first called it was not so deep, as the roof was only a few inches above my head when I stood up. It was not round, but rather a hexagon like a honeycomb cell. The ceiling had been plastered over in a dull yellow ochre material which had seen better days as it was mottled by shades of brown and soot. The plaster was cracked in places with a few missing areas although the floor was clean of debris, so evidently someone still cared for this place. There appeared to be a carved serpent twining around, looking more like a thick green caterpillar darkened by soot. I had to turn around to follow its meanderings. In the flickering light it appeared almost alive as it weaved its way amongst the cracks until it was head to head with a dragon, which appeared to have been a brick-red colour once but was now faded. I felt I had seen something like it before, then I realised it looked like the heraldic arms of Somerset. Was this a coincidence?

I began in my mind's eye to focus on the reality of this pit. It was indeed intriguing, yes, but there was no reason for me to be fearful. Carved around the edge of the ceiling I made out faded sea creatures, a fish, maybe a turtle and even a lobster.

From a small ventilation shaft in the ceiling a narrow beam of light slanted across the floor. Round the hole were set a circle of heart shapes forming a rose. The weak beam of light drew my attention to the floor where the intertwining circles of a Mandorla or Vesica Pisces were laid out on the hardened surface of peat and clay. One circle had been drawn with white or grey clay and the other was in red ochre. I knelt to touch the circle and found it was an inlay of clay hardened and smoothed by time and laid by ancient hands. Here on the floor was the eternal symbol of interaction and interdependence of opposing worlds and forces, expression of the mystic tension of complementary opposites. This is what I had so often seen at Chalice Well, the other side to the modern forlorn White Spring.

My mind raced away to what I knew of mathematics, and the significance of the two equilateral triangles formed by the intersections. I could repeat out loud that, 'the ratio of the height of the Vesica Pisces to the width across its centre is the square root of three.' That three was therefore a magical number—but maths was never my strong point, and sacred geometry was the realm of experts like Merlin. But I did not mind betting that this pit, now elevated in my mind to 'sacred chamber', would be based upon sacred proportions. My Polish friend, a good needlewoman, once introduced me to the Slav Flower. It symbolises the Sun God and is seen everywhere in ancient Slav mythology and folk patterns. When extended many times it becomes the Flower of Life, a symbol first seen in ancient Assyria. Snippets like 'it forms the golden mean, the basis for the proportion at Stonehenge and all Gothic cathedrals' sprang to my mind. I vowed to look into this further when I got back, and to look at embroidery on folk costumes more carefully.

The walls were covered in symbols I did not recognise, a meaningless set of squiggles beyond my knowledge but I did discern that they were in groups. There were twelve regular sets that I assumed were the months. There were repetitive markers eight times around the six walls. Okay, I thought, here are the quarter days and the cross quarters and a bit of geometry set against proportion. Next there were obviously feminine figures on opposite walls, one red and one white, like queens in opposition. Their nipped-in narrow waists and upraised arms made them look more like insects or bees than people.

Suddenly Merlin's voice breathed into my ear.

'Just like Alice in Wonderland, my dear.'

His voice startled me, but he was right. I indeed might have fallen down a rabbit hole. I wondered if Lewis Carroll had been in this Avalon. He had been a strange man. Was he one of Merlin's shapeshifting friends? After all, Lewis Carroll, or the real man Charles Dodgson, had been good at mathematics, he was a romantic and a member of the pre-Raphaelite movement, hence keen on Arthurian tales. Despite being a clergyman he was early into the Society for Psychical Research and an early photographer. He also maintained a childlike way of openness to the beauty of nature and the simplicity of children. Had he known Merlin, or met him? All Dodgson's players seemed to be here, writ on the walls and ceiling. Had his wit invented names for them—perhaps with the help of a puff of weed or poppy?

The crone who until now had been silent, now spoke. It was as though she had read my mind.

'Others have been to Avalon, my dear, and some came long before the Arthur after whom you enquire. It is true the spirit whom you call Merlin has a fondness for this place because it is a place of solar and earthly power. It is a place where the impersonal driving force of all living beings is more manifest, more concentrated and available. Here the gods and spirits are able to manifest and meet people of the Lilith blood line, whom they can inhabit or even cohabit with as they used to do. This is a place where the plants and trees can manifest to some people in fairy form, appearing as light energies; where spirit forms like elves are seen and spoken with. There are guardian spirits of this place and straight energy lines in which the spirits travel from one power place to another. Some have more power than others, and subtly drive human nature for good or ill. The power can be used by anyone who knows how to harness it. But whilst it is impersonal the entities who use that power, whether human or spirit, have different agendas with outcomes for good or bad.

'I am Enid, Lady of Joy, once called virtuous and faithful. I have seen 102 summers, but this winter my old bones tell me will be my last. I was the youngest of the sisterhood of the Ladies of the Lake, just twenty summers old when we rowed the body of Arthur across the Lake to his resting place in the hollow hill. Now I am the last but one to have the breath of life still within me.

'I watched you carefully as your mind flitted from one connection to another. You are unlike me for I like to sit by the seashore and listen to the sound of the sea and tides and the rise and fall of the river waters.' The crone held something in her outstretched hand.

'See here, take my shell and place it to your ear. Can you hear the sea now?'

I could heard the swishing of waves sighing through pebbles, and there was more. As I held the shell to my ear, wave after wave of shifting perfumes came to my consciousness like a sedative or hypnotic. A deep earthy smell led my mind to the softness of peach and the smile of mandarin, whilst a strong smell of rose captivated my nose for just a second and then was gone. I leaned back, pressing against the cold stone, as my mind emptied and became still.

The crone began to keen and tap a tambour in steady rhythm. I listened in my inner self, gently rocking back and forth to the rhythm, my attention held by this wave of divine fragrance. She had truly entranced me by this perfume of a goddess's presence. Like a seeping smoke the fragrance opened me to the spirit residing in the crone. She began to speak about herself.

'Joy is here by the waters of the ever changing Lake and Sea. My home is of the four rivers, but it is the wandering Carey that intrigues me most. I hold the golden child within me to be born at due time when the moon is at its fullest.'

I stared unblinking at the crone as she slowly transformed to a young woman with blonde hair falling into long braids around her shoulders. In my blurred vision she seemed to wear a top garment of deep red wool over a kirtle of rose pink. Everything seemed soft and clothed in moonlight. Her lilting voice continued.

'This is the quiet time when leaves begin to fall, when green turns to be touched by russet hue. Leaves begin to curl and some fall still green but dry. I sit by the Great Estuary where Sabrinna roils from time to time as her waves fight the moon tide. I reflect upon the sea's bounty and its harvest, of the sound of the ocean still carried by its shells when I am far away on land. From the foam of the sea sweet

Venus came floating on a sea shell. I have lived within a lustrous shell of delicate pink and pearl, hidden from most eyes who do not see my beauty. For my beauty is the end of growth, my season is when the sun lessens its power. Once I was poor on the Isle of Sheep; now I have grown rich with the man I love in familial loyalty.

'Is this like you Barley? Are you the quiet season of reflection? I think not. After all, though we share the same ability to emulate the cyclical power of nature's seasons, we are all different women. We share a lust for living and for receiving potential within us. We all share the capacity to bewitch men, to frighten them and lend their latent force to the will of the gods. For the divine feminine is a creative force, a re-creative force, that nurtures the ancestral memory of blood that carries the life force of spirit. Every man knows the death he feels when his seed is spent in woman and when sometimes he vents his loss in anger when his power is betrayed and wasted. We women alone can raise this power to ecstasy and rapture to exceed all human thought in unison of purpose. The purpose is for the spirit within us to be empowered, for the crops to yield, as power passes to above and below.

'Look closely, Barley, at the base of the Vesica. You see there a simple small hole in the ground. The light advances to the hole or retreats from it according to the wheel of the year. This is the spirit hole from which our ancestors and spirits rise, the sacred place of memory where we of earth and water have come from. Upon this sacred space Arthur lay with his sister Morgause, entwined in the rite of sacred marriage, confirming his sovereignty as High King amongst the tribes.

'Morgause was Queen by birth and marriage, but she was a free woman with the blood of elves deep in her veins. The elves are ever lustful and so was she. She had all the allure, cunning and experience of a full woman to satisfy and draw young Arthur to this place. Just as the earth twists and turns and presses together to make earth lights, so their coupling made a force of power that drove swords to hew the

Picts, Scots, Saxons and all barbarians from the Sacred Albion.'

The crone paused. I thought of the cliffs by the Summerland seashore, where the bands of rock show the turmoil of the past, the writhing of the Great Mother beneath the parting heavens. There shale oil showed, and fossil trees and shells; even footprints of the giant lizards that once walked here could be seen. Smugglers used these beaches to hide their wares. These amazing folded cliffs and ancient pavements with fossil trees were so profound to thinking men that the Celts simply called this place the Cliff or Kilve. Truly such earthquakes in times immemorial, with fire and water beyond the brain's conception, had formed this earth. Such power did indeed lie in the rocks and stones from which we humans took our form.

The crone glanced toward the spirit or ancestor hole.

'I press two white crystals hard together my dear and light comes within them by simple pressure. So you can comprehend the power of place in Avalon, where new water pulls the greenery swiftly beneath its greedy surface, turning sediment to peat. When compressed further it turns to black liquid, or hard black stone which some say can burn. I can read your every thought; nothing is hidden from me. I know what primal energy lies at the base of your spine, and what can be released.'

I felt my thoughts invaded and my privacy violated.

'Piezzo electricity is all you are talking about with your two stones, it's not a mystery,' I said, feeling irritated. 'Watches run on vibration you know, it's all science.'

The crone cackled and stopped her rhythmic tambour beating.

'My darling you are so right. I do not know the words you use but Merlin says that science and magic meet in time and space; that your time knows less and less yet more and more—which is one of his riddles. Avalon is a power place so let me show you what you cannot see, but that is here watching you. Tell me, doubting woman, what is this?'

A scuffling came from the hole and suddenly came the smell of wet dog. Suddenly standing before me stood a slavering huge black dog. It had malignant, hard emotionless eyes, seeming to look upon me as prey, nothing more. Its tongue hung loose. On its haunches it scraped its sheath along the floor. It placed a paw on my shoulder pushing me against the wall, forcing me down from the ledge upon which I sat. I was terrified, my knees pressed against the dog's chest, overwhelmed by the dog's reek and constant growling. I wet myself and felt urine running down my leg, yet no sound came, all I could do was whimper.

'Don't worry woman, he won't bite. He wants to mate with you!' I screamed and I must have fainted. The next thing I knew I was seated back on the ledge as though nothing had happened. I felt my skirt and found it dry, no pee. The crone shouted at me.

'Was that real, or just your imagination—or was it pure magic, science woman, you who are so clever? Was it real or did it happen in another dimension? It may have felt real to you, but it wasn't real here in this realm. Have you not heard of the Barguest, the Black Dog? Well?'

I cleared my throat.

'I have heard of the Girt Dog of Langport and the hound of the Baskervilles, is that what it was? Was it a nightmare or an apparition? Tell me.'

'The Black Dog is energy. As you know, it is part of the landscape of Glastonbury. Yesterday he was manifest as Arthur's dog Cabal, only Cabal was white. Hence, as I said to you, energy manifests as you wish to see it.'

'But I didn't want to see a black dog, you forced it upon me,' I responded.

'No my dear, I created an anticipation and you provided form, from your fear of this place and your fear of revealing yourself—and perhaps from your unfulfilled loins. Avalon is a place of powerful change. Here you will be taken to your soul being and be transformed, if you so desire.

'Now see me as I am, as a powerful being, not as this crone-like charade which unfortunately turns to dust. Scent me, smell me, feel me and I will touch you.'

The smell of earth, peach and rose returned and once more overwhelmed me, sinking into my flesh and bones, into my mind and spirit.

The walls swam in a circle. The tambour started again, and the symbols gradually turned to colours, then took form as women sat within arched windows. I looked at them entranced and they smiled back at me. I saw Enid and laughed, realising what I had just seen: the seasons had passed before my eyes. I had seen sun and rain, snow and hail. I had seen corn grow and the spring flowers, the autumn leaves and the cattle and sheep. I had seen wild horses, and once a unicorn, and salmon run beneath signs in the starry heavens. I lay flat on my back, floating ever upward to the ceiling, spinning slowly through time.

The vision faded and I awakened. I had been in a trance. I spoke out loud.

'I have seen the circle of the seasons. I have seen the power of the vortex of Avalon, that flows from the divine feminine, the Great Mother in her various forms, and the spirit gods. I have been away with the fairies.'

'So you have my dear,' spoke Enid. 'You have learned that our time in Avalon is cyclical not linear. The seasons will come again as every farmer knows. Just as Arthur has gone so he will come again, and so will you and I as we become ancestors to those yet to come. So in Avalon we take our opportunity as life presents it. We seek our carnal pleasure, for that is what results in happiness and fulfilment. But we do not practice harm or wish evil to another. We do not squander our bodies, for when we depart, what value is a fortune if it must be left behind? We join the cycle of generation, of work, pleasure and spending ourself and our treasure for merit. Think of this in Avalon my dear. The fairies always dance in circles. The circle dance is all.'

6

Merlin's Rant

And so Barley's journey had begun in earnest. It was not the going to Avalon which was important, it was the being there. To be there fully she had to understand herself, and be alive to what was around her. She had to get used to being attuned to her senses. So time turned its wheel.

'You live in an age of distraction, where everything is in the now. Appearance is what your culture is all about. Your mode of existence is in the unreality of a digital image, a virtual world confined to a screen. An image is viewed in a small square or enlarged on a big screen, and its reality is lost. Horror becomes a commonplace. Conscience is seared and deadened by the presentation of abnormality as acceptable. Individual responsibility is lost to the mass of the collective. There is no essence to your materialistic society. Hence people like you take refuge in myths that draw you to another world which seems unreal but has authentic existence on another plane.' Merlin was in one of his ranting moods.

Barley had learned not to argue with Merlin once this mood settled on him. His rants, as she called them, came and went like a summer shower. Often they were outbursts of his frustration. He had seen everything that time had to offer, so he knew the value of history. His proposition was that the young had no awareness of history, and it was important that they learn about it. Otherwise they would always be lured by the promise of tomorrow, which was the Oligarch's central theme—always the promise of tomorrow, not the present reality. Learning history took time, so young people had to be distracted with fiction, with playing computer games, which were no more than the silly old bang, bang your dead games translated into the 21st century. In contrast, understanding the past made you whole. Merlin preferred chess.

So to humour him while he was talking to the air, Barley settled down to listen. She didn't have a good book to read, having left hers by the apple tree a long time ago, so she may as well be his audience.

'Glastonbury in your time still weaves its way between myth and reality. The gods still watch there in Avalon, but recreation of the mythos is superseded by the phoney; so the real healing power of the waters and the land has been discredited by mountebank shamans. The meeting places are full of tutors and mentors, leaders and acolytes, students and ardent followers; they are the haunt of phoneys, charlatans and drum bangers. I am largely ignored, in my trees and my sacred place amongst the apple trees. We are bypassed—me, Arthur, the Lady and Avalon itself—in favour of plastic fairies with fixed smiles and fixed wings. Glastonbury has become a place where velvet robes are sold to budding Wiccans and pentacles are worn upside down by accident. Many seek Morganna and I, but they are taken via India or the Cherokee or diverted to Scandinavia.

'Truth is not found in mass production but in the craft of true bread, in the woodcarver's skill, in the poet's words and in the per-fumer's skill to call the spirits to your being. It is more difficult in your time to find the good people, the old people, the fair folk of Glastonbury, than before. The lament for Arthur should be heard. My Lady should be praised as in the Immortal Hour which reflects the truth of Avalon so well. The portals are still there, nurtured by spirit but not so easy to see. True, I am jaundiced and cynical today, for I am old. Yet inside I am young and in touching distance of you, if you wish to seek me in the sacred grove in your time. It was not by chance that we met in one such portal.' Merlin was musing now.

'Here in Avalon on this Island in the Great Lake was born the epic of Arthur and the Lady of the Lake. He is owned by these Summer Lands and by Cornwall and Duntagel as well as Cumbria, but it was here in Glastonbury where his heart was laid to rest and where his sovereignty was confirmed. He was returned here to lie in rest and from here he will be sent forth, the once and future king. In due time the Lady of the Lake will empower him again. Then she will rise with the restless waters, however hard men try to tame them.

Glastonbury, as Avalon, preceded Arthur's own fame. He knew that well, for after all he got his learning from me. It is I, Merlin, with My Lady of the Lake, who am most closely associated with this sacred place of earthy and watery energy. We have seen these seven sacred islands from the beginning when the seas rose and the springs opened. At that time the gods were banished from the land. Then these sacred islands rose to reflect the seven heavenly stars. Those seven stars make up the Great Bear and the lesser egotistical She Bear. Together they point to the Star of the Sea, whose significance was recorded when a prophet said long ago: 'I will ascend to heaven; I will set my throne on high above the stars; in the far reaches of the north I will sit on the mount of assembly.' That is the place of the Gods and Goddesses beyond the stars. These seven pointers light a pathway to the astral plains and Caer Sidi.'

Barley yawned behind her hand, not wanting to ignore Merlin. She agreed with him to some extent that she had found less of the romance of the Arthurian age in Glastonbury than she had expected. Not even the Grail was featured as she had hoped. Merlin however was clearly fed up with the weather, which was dripping water from a leaden sky.

He needed the sun to bring out his good humour and creativity. He had been working with powdered rocks for the ink the monks used, and also fusing pigments into coloured glass. The fumes had added to his grouchiness. Today he was thinking, and thinking always led to musings then rantings.

'So Barley, my Arthur was finally brought here in the sacred barge by the nine queens or sisters of the lake and wheel. On the lakeside the three queens in sacred quarter service waited with the tribal women keening and singing the song of Arthur. The twelve, now complete as in the cosmic order, led the mournful procession to lay him for his long rest in the hollow hill. He was my Arthur for I made him what he was, the once and future king, waiting the time when his white dragon bloodline will save this land again from those who would consume it to a whimper of sterility. True, once in a time not far from yours I saw the white and red chequerboard whirling, spiralling high in blue skies, spitting fire in a hurricane storm to save this people. But their power was betrayed and they left for the mountain of the sleeping knight. In Arthur's life he was known both as King of the Northern Kingdoms and King of the Southern. He became Chief Warlord of the Britons, Dux Bellorum in the Latin language. The strife between the North and South, so damaging to humankind, plays to the purpose of the Oligarch; for disunity is his strength, the battle between right and wrong his powerplay. Arthur's strength was in the unity of diversity. Like his father Uther he had a temper and was savage in war, hence he was feared.

'So of Arthur, or Artur meaning the bear. I knew the name could be played as Artorius, the Roman clan name meaning noble and courageous. By a simple name I created him as a symbol for the tribes, as the totem bear; and for the Romans a noble patrician of any persuasion. He was my greatest triumph.'

Merlin paused, rubbing his chin ruefully. He had cut himself

68

shaving with a Roman iron razor which had lost its edge (he lost his 21st century version somewhere). Dabbing himself with a spider web and herb concoction, he peered in the mirror.

'Did you know Barley,' he continued, 'that the word barbarian means unbarbered or unshaved. Clean shaved means civilisation. Julius Caesar was so fastidious he had every whisker tweezed out every day. Brave man our Julius. The Emperor Hadrian who built the wall had a short beard because he had a lousy complexion, so beards caught on for a while, but we are back now to shaving fashion and so was Arthur. No beards please. Useless but interesting bits of information Barley.'

'What about the women?' asked Barley.

'The latest craze just catching on is for women to pluck out all eyebrows, the temple area and even eye lashes. Yes, I mean it! Look at early medieval painting. Don't ask me why Barley, I have no idea. And before you ask, wax, resin and honey depilatories exist, and scrubs and pumice. It all depends upon where you are in society as to what you use. People like to be clean and look their best, unless they are mentally deranged or disturbed in some way. So there you have it.' He finished patting and daubing.

'Now where was I? Ah yes, Arthur. When I think about it now, a few years later, perhaps I did lose some magical power to Nimue, whom some call Vivienne. I was infatuated by the flattery of my own mind and the whiles of a greed-filled young beauty exercising her charming power. It was my jealous but true dark lover Morganna who led Nimue to her fickle ways and my fate. It is always a problem when spirit manifests itself in human form and consummates. True a golden child may have come to join the pantheon of lesser gods and heroes, but my Arthur was more than these because he was truly man and truly King among men.

'I told you as we started out together that I would write my own words. But words are only symbols, sounds reflecting what we have spoken face to face. Maybe a later reader shall see me through these pages, discerning wit from wisdom and fact from fiction. Let us see, Barley, how this turns out. For what is behind the words is what is meant and this requires understanding and interpretation. Like the pearl inside a shell it has to be sought and found. This is the problem of books learned by rote and taken literally word by word: they become immutable like stone and cannot adapt to the winds of time and season.

'Archaeologists and academics look for evidence to prove a myth. But what can they expect to find? These people don't write, they tell stories; they don't build temples, they worship in places such as springs and lakes, woods and fields. Suppose they find post holes. Was this circle a hut, a set of carved figures like totem poles, or a sacred grove? It goes on and on. No evidence, so the stories from the past must be untrue. How do you prove a myth? Best in my opinion to simply accept the story and learn what you can from it.'

As Merlin spoke and Barley listened intently she caught a glimpse of the house fairy, who liked to be called a domovik, not a goblin or a brownie. The cold of the darker nights had come and it was his job to keep the fire bright. His name was Peterkin Thumblesticks, a corruption of his true name which he said was unpronounceable in English. Merlin had found him wandering cold and lost in the steppes, far from the banks of the broad river which divides Europe from Asia. This was when the city of Silys was destroyed and the fairy's human family were killed by the brutal German Gotthoi.

Peterkin was a small dark brown fairy with a solemn face and long bushy beard. He was hairy, a bit like a small bear with long arms and legs. He was devoted to Merlin and somewhat jealous of Wenna who did some of what he regarded as his chores.

At first Barley had seen him as a larger hairy spider scuttling off into a corner. Of course this she now knew was her rational assumption. Once she had learned to see what she saw and not impose what she thought she saw, Peterkin had appeared. What intrigued her was that she could think him bigger or smaller (shades of Alice she had thought). His maximum size was about one foot high, his real size, but she saw him about six inches which was her favourite size. She now knew that when the logs were red and they suddenly collapsed the sparks flew it was him poking the fire. He was not keen on the job because sometimes being hairy he got a bit singed. Of course the Domevoi were dying out because people mistook them for big black spiders and trod on them.

He was happy now, gently humming and playing on his comb like a small harp. He enjoyed listening to this bit of history which he knew was coming, for it touched on his lost family.

7

The Coming of the Dragons

And so, my friend Barley, we must travel north to Bremetennacum Veteranorum, as the Romans called their camp by the Ribble River. You will call it Ribchester, or even 'camp of the veterans.' Camp? Well a town really, no tents, except when the Second Legion first arrived there in the conquest a few hundred years ago. But later, when the First Sarmatian Cavalry Wing of the Sixth Victrix Legion arrived, with five thousand fighting men, such a number of soldiers demanded a big town.

Oh don't go on about long words and boring facts again Barley. When you read this later, as others will, you will need to see some facts. Facts maketh the myth! Anyway when these Sarmatians came they brought everything; there were all their horses for a start, then their wives and children, the camp followers, and all the trappings of a town on the move, about eighteen thousand people in all. This was a small migration. And they brought their own myths and gods. They worshipped the sword thrust into the ground, the chalice and the blade symbolising fertility.

Where was Sarmatia? In today's terms it spread from Poland down into Romania and Hungary and upward into the Ukraine, and earlier into Central Asia. The world of horses and grasslands.

Ah, I remember their first contingent so very well. The scale armour sparkling like a thousand mirrors in the sunshine, with column after column of horsemen riding by. The smell of sweat, leather and horse dung all hanging in the air. Their horses were larger than the native ponies, and all caparisoned with silver on the harness and great red tassels dangling from the leathers. Some were coated in scale armour like their riders. They had coloured geometric tribal symbols on their shields. Likewise their tamga and their bunczuk horse tails were held high.

The long lances they carried had pennons of white and red, some tabards were chequerboard white and red. But above all, some standards bore frightening dragonheads and their tails were like windsocks, that carried the sound of the wind in them when they charged. An eerie noise with the thunder of hooves. On their backs flags and feathers rustled, giving the appearance of flight like eagles and dragons. They were a proud troop of warriors that day so long ago, a sight to stir the heart.

These Sarmatians were specialist soldiers. They were not like the lightly equipped Gauls, the Thracians and other auxiliaries. These people were select heavy cavalry, these Sarmatians, Alans, Dacians and Wends as they were known later. But think on their dragon pennons, their dragon look. There were no dragons in England before these people, who were born of the dragonblood of Lilith and of Tubal. Draconaria the Romans called them—dragons. You would call them lancers and in the Middle Ages they called them knights.

What, you don't know about Lilith? Incredible. Well briefly, according to Jewish mythology, Adam had a wife before Eve, whose name was Lilith. The story goes like this. When the blessed God created the first man, whom he formed out of the ground, alone and without a companion, God said, 'It is not good that the man should be alone.' And therefore he created a woman, also out of the ground, and named her Lilith. They immediately began to contend with each other for superiority. Adam said: 'It behoves thee to be obedient; I am to rule over thee.' Then Lilith replied, 'We are of a perfect equality; for we are both formed out of the same earth.' So neither would submit to the other. Lilith, realising this, uttered the Shem-hamphorash, that is, she pronounced the Oligarch's name Jehovah, which should never be done, and instantly she was blown away through the air. Refusing to submit to Adam, she was taken away, hidden, written out of history. Lilith taught wisdom to Adam like a serpent dragon, or transforming to an owl in a tree, a creature of the dark, an erotic lover; and he could never forget her. If you want to see how others imagine her, think of those who in your time praise Rhiannon; or look at the work of Rosetti called 'Lady Lilith' and, as Goethe wrote, 'Beware of her fair hair, for she excels all women in the magic of her locks, and when she twines them round a young man's neck she will not ever set him free again.' But I don't want to digress. Let us just say these Sarmatians had her dragonblood, as probably do you!

Anyway the Romans were always having trouble with the terrifying painted Picts, the fiery Scots from Ireland and the big hulking Saxon raiders in the North, so these cavalrymen were dispersed quite quickly to the Wall in the North and into Wales to keep out the Irish. The rather imaginative Picts and Caledonians thought them godlike. The tribesmen saw these scaly armoured creatures all shining in the morning light, their horses puffing with breath condensing in the cool air— no wonder they ran from these dragons!

And never forget the Sarmatian women. The Greek historian Herodotus wrote of these people, 'No girl shall wed till she has killed a man in battle.' The status of women in this society was one of equality and mutual respect. They were keepers of the divine fire, the hearth. When the men fought it was the women who maintained the traditions of balance. They knew the value of warcraft in the defence of home, the pursuit of fairness in motherhood, and the nurture of nature.

The wheel of time turned and the Legions left, but their descendants stayed. Legionaries settled and farmed, and as with all migrant communities intermarriage came about to a limited extent but also closed communities occurred, maintaining traditions from the past. The Sarmatians were horse people and remained horse breeders with their own military ways and traditions.

After the legions left, the great chaos began and local warlords squabbled for local power. It was easy for wealthy people to buy mercenaries and later bribe them with land. The Romans had done this many times but under strict control. Soon, however, these barbarian mercenaries found rich plunder: silver, slaves and good farmland. So the wars began. Saxons, Jutes, Angles in the east and in the north the ever dangerous Picts and Scots from Ireland pushing to command and pillage Britain.

Now why should I be telling you all this? Because I am the champion of Albion, the inheritance of Troy, if I am anything at all. And, as that troubadour poet Robert de Boron wrote, I am a shape-shifter, joker and magician; so pay attention to my truth and discern what was real then and what is not real now, or of course the other way around.

This was a time when Albion was subsumed by clashing cultures. When native fought immigrant, when the rich stole from the poor, when leaders betrayed the people whom they led.

I had to shift from one manifestation to another, bestowing favour upon whomever would represent and serve me well. I roam about seeking the servant spies of the Oligarch and setting mine own against those who would such order bring that all change ceases and time is frozen in religious zeal. For I exist in times and other times again, and you have need of those who tell the past in ways that transform the present. Sweet Albion, am I leaving you behind? Have I left you far behind for a foreign land? Albion you are free and always will be, by my will.

As you have seen around you, when the legions left the Roman lifestyle continued, especially for the patrician classes. But slowly it went downhill. The departure of the Romans did not go unnoticed by the Picts, Scots, Irish and especially the Saxons, who saw Britain as a prosperous country ripe for plunder. Raids and minor invasions became common, demanding organised military action at a local level. So as time went by the country degenerated back to the way it was four hundred years earlier. In the South-West the tribes had anyway never settled entirely into Roman ways. Britain became an entity in name only, and no longer a cohesive unit.

Among the warlords Uther Pendragon became the most famed. I needed his bloodline joined to the Old People: those of magic, the sea people and the Celts. What better bloodline could there be than that of Sarmatia, the dragonblood, joined to that of the people of the Cornovii, a people never conquered by Rome and faithful to Avalon, to their Grain Goddess and to Cerne. The unity of pagan and Christian was an idea proposed by the Lady herself. I needed the North and South to unite, a mighty knighthood like the draconaria of the past.

You know the story well in many versions and media, mostly fiction, and I am not repeating a version here. But let me be clear, Arthur existed. Nothing irritates me more than the late 20th and 21st century academics who are quite sure Arthur did not exist. What arrogant assumption! Their reasoning, requiring wily monks and historians plotting to invent a hero just to have one to boast about. Do they not think that people would have noticed this hero before, this novel fictional character of the academics? Try going among the people here, Barley, and say 'Did you know, Captain America saved you from the Romans?' They would say, 'Funny, my grandad never said that, you are just making it up sunshine—clear off!' Ask outside if Arthur existed and they will tell you he is buried in the sacred cave, and the Christians will tell you they have plans to move him to their holy ground.

If it was not for Arthur, England would have simply been a Germanised country. He bought time for assimilation, unification, conversion, education and the traditions of respect and values. These are what made Great Britain a place of free people with dignity, pride and nobility of spirit, from Troy to the magic of the people of Dana, from the dash and poetry of the Celts to the stolid courage and work of the Saxons. Only the lowland Scots never quite understood loyalty to the new nations that emerged.

Arthur, true to the traditions of the Sarmatians, drew his sword of kingship from the earth or stone or anvil. The blade emerged from the clay mould into which molten rock had been poured. Time changes the story, for the resultant blade was beaten on the anvil. This conferred the right to kingship. This short sword was called Clarent, the sword of fire, for it was dark as though blackened by fire. It had a cross-like hilt, was work-hardened and had a ring at the pommel that contained an amber stone. Sometimes Clarent was called the cowards sword because Mordred used it to kill Arthur. Last time I saw it Dr. John Dee had it in Krakow. That would have been about 1584 I think.

That event made Arthur war leader; the Saxons called him King. Arthur needed more authority than this. He needed authority and the authenticity to make patterns in the chaos. At first he was young and untested, so I devised a scheme to give him a divine right to kingship. True, Clarent was acknowledged by the Celts as they thought it might have belonged to Cerne or perhaps Gwynn ap Nudd. But I needed a simple clarification of divine right. Clarent was wholly male side, something to be grabbed and disputable, strident with nothing to do with civil sovereignty and authority. So My Lady and I thought and talked about this, and I was tasked to settle the possible future disputation of his authority.

8

Swordplay

n ow, as you know, the Lady is a composite figure of the
twelve and the one. They maintain the sacred fire and the
ceremonies for the fertility of the soil. Each is chosen as a
consort by the tribe, or sometimes captured in combat, and each serves
a goddess as their representative on earth. They are free to take as
many lovers as their nature wishes or the spirit within them demands.

I had some sympathy for Morgan, for she was the daughter of
Gorlois the Duke, a local king of Cornwall and Dintagel, one of the
greatest strongholds of Britain. She always saw Arthur as a usurper,
as did her sister Morgause whom I shall tell of later. As it was,
Morganna and I became lovers. Oh, her dark hair and eyes. She had
no need of magic to enchant me; it was her blue eyes.

Now I know the sexual appetite of Morgan well and she knows
mine. To be lost in desire amid a cloud of incense, clothed in the warm
opulence of satin and silk—this suits us both. Not for us the cold
moonlit night and the soft moss, or the so called fun of making love
on the wet sand of a seashore or a secret rose bower—that choice is
for the others, each one then to their own aroma of desire and erotic
fulfilment.

In our pillow talk we decided we needed an event to draw attention
to Arthur's unique qualities as a youthful High King or Warlord, a

'chosen one'. We needed good PR, as you would say. Morganna took the idea to Our Lady and she sanctioned it. So I brought back a sword from Damascus with a cross hilt and damascene steel blade. You know the blade type, the one with wavy lines on it that shimmer. This special steel was made in India and the technology required had not reached Britain, so it was the first of its type to be seen here. The ripple effect on the blade catches the sun and splits it into a myriad lights and sparkles. It was light for its size, and I had engraved on one side 'Take me up' and on the other 'Cast me away'.

I had encouraged Arthur to draw on his greatest support which was here amongst the tribes in the West. He had begun work with a band of younger warriors in refortifying a strategically placed ancient Iron Age hill fort not so far from Glastonbury, at a place called Cantmael. The strategy was to rebuild a string of forts to protect the heartland, then move north. Cantmael was destined to weave its own special legend, and later writers confused this great war castle with Viroconium, the civitas or administrative metropolis mouldering but still useful in the middle of the Marches.

Arthur had never entered the sacred marsh lands before, so I had travelled the few miles south and persuaded him he should be initiated into the old ways which would cement the western tribes to his cause, both down here and in the pagan borderlands of the northwest. And so he agreed to come with me to Avalon, the secret place of the ancestors.

Now Arthur, as it is with young men, had never really had a good sword of his own for the battles he knew would come. Clariant, the state sword, was usable but not the best for a fight, especially if cavalry tactics were to be resumed. So on our way up to Avalon one evening I took him out on Greylake. We paddled onto the lake in a coracle, ostensibly to catch a fish for supper. Now in your day, due to drainage, the same place is farmland; but then it was a deep mere or tarn, black with peat at the reed edge and out on the surface silver from the reflected sky. Of course I had arranged for the coracle to be waiting on the shore.

We the conspirators had taken one of the maidens of the sisterhood, Argante—she passed over not so long ago. She was then very young, just a child, naive and pliable. We dressed her in white with gold threads, as befitted a chosen damsel. We taught her how to submerge underwater and breathe through a hollow reed. She was waiting, hidden among the reeds by the water's edge, until she saw Arthur and me in the boat.

That fateful evening I took Arthur by the old Roman road to Greylake. The road runs upward from the long port; it takes the ridge, avoiding the Zoylands and bypassing Avalon itself, curving around the possible military pinch-point by the two hills called the twins in the Great Star Circle, it re-joins the wooded ridge before reaching the four cross turn toward the moor. This was where Arthur got his first real view of Avalon to his left, rising like a woman laying on her side in a pool of shimmering water. He was spellbound.

We reached the lake. A biggish coracle was bobbing in the wavelets by the shore, blown up by the evening breeze. I am not an expert with a paddle, but after going round in circles a few times with Arthur complaining, I got the hang of it and paddled over to the reed beds where the bitterns boom. What Arthur saw next changed history just as I planned, but his unforeseen decision changed my plan—and was his loss.

Yes dear it was I who did not see what was coming. I thought him more grown up than he was.

Argante was right down in the water hidden amongst the reeds. As our boat drew near she raised her arm and held the sword high. Arthur saw her ghostly arm rise from the water, clad in white silk interwoven with gold and silver thread, clutching the sword in its jewelled gold scabbard. It caught the light of the setting sun like a fire jewel as it was being waved about. This fire streak effect came about because Argante was shivering, near frozen to death in the cold water, and in addition the sword was heavy for this slight girl. So there it was weaving back and forth for Arthur to see.

Then came the next part of my plan. A beautiful woman appeared to walk or glide over the surface of the lake toward us. She was dressed in deep blue and black, the light catching the large number of jewels she wore around her neck. The sparkle from the jewellery obscured her veiled face. Arthur was already spooked, and when he saw this woman, who to him was like an apparition, he was stunned.

I told him she was the Lady of the Lake, and that he must ask her for the sword. Of course, the Lady at this point in time, on the cusp of October/November, was my co-conspirator and lover Morgan, known as Le Fay.

Doing as he was told because he was in a bit of a funk, Arthur called out asking her if he may have the sword. Argante had to keep bringing it down as it was so heavy, so that it slipped in an out of the water tantalizingly, increasing Arthur's agitation.

The Lady, the fairy apparition, nodded said he should take the sword, that it was called Caliburn and it would serve him well. The name simply meant steel hard, alluding to its special manufacture, supposedly forged here in Avalon. As it was the only one in Britain no one was going to gainsay this!

'It is yours, Arthur,' the Lady called, 'but it must be returned to me when you die. No other man may keep this sword, for it holds poison to all except of the blood.'

We nosed into the reeds to pull closer, nearly drowning poor Argante as she later told us, and she gamely held the sword up. Arthur leaned over, nearly upending the coracle, grabbed the sword and fell back. In the process he toppled over, but thank the gods he fell into the coracle, now bobbing about violently. The sword was protected by a beautiful leather scabbard inlaid with gold and with precious gems so he did not cut his hand. The hand that had held it slipped beneath the water and I quickly pulled the coracle back to let Argante slip away. Morgan vanished into the reeds. The water on which she seemed to walk was only about a few inches deep, concealing an old part-submerged trackway. Arthur had no idea of these watery paths and their ways.

He laid the sword across his knees in its precious bejewelled scabbard and whilst I paddled back he half-drew the blade and examined the words engraved upon it. And now I made my mistake—all my paddling had addled my senses. I asked Arthur which he preferred, the sword or the scabbard?

'Oh Merlin, how can you ask? This is the most beautiful of swords. Is it mine to keep?' He waved it about in the last rays of the sun, setting the coracle bobbing about. I struggled not to tip us into the water.

'But what of the scabbard,' I responded with urgency, 'is it not the finest in the land?'

'A mere bauble Merlin, too showy. The blade is the real power, not the scabbard into which it plunges.'

When Arthur spoke these fateful words I almost heard Morgana hiss with rage. She had slaved long to create this scabbard and placed all her healing into it, all the power of the sisterhood.

'The sword sheathed is a symbol of peace, Arthur. That is what we want. If you had chosen the scabbard it would have kept you safe in battle. As it is, it can heal but not save you. But no, you cannot keep the sword. It is on loan and must be returned to the Lady in due time.'

By the time we reached shore it was dark. We lit a fire and ate the oatcakes I had brought. Its flickering flames attracted fish, so Arthur speared one with a stick whittled to a point and we had a campfire supper. In the night we could hear the distant howl of the Girt Black Dog. We decided not to risk the sodden moor marsh; instead, using the coracle as a lean-to shelter, we camped there on the lakeshore.

Next day we set off for Avalon and entered the sacred temenos by crossing the Brue at Pomparles Bridge. We could see the Isle of Women to the left and I pointed out the pattern of the land as we walked. Being of Roman patrician thinking, if not class, Arthur asked where Joseph of Arimathea had landed. I told him it was virtually where we were standing.

'Look to your right,' I told him. 'There is the Sacred Thorn grown from Joseph's staff.' He peered upward to a thicket of trees lining the ridge.

'Anyone of those thorns in particular?' Arthur joked. 'The Christians do love a legend, at least the newly-arrived ones.'

'The original Christians were quite different,' I responded philosophically. 'They used to allow a bit of informal chaos and debate, but since the latest arrivals from Rome they are getting more formal and controlling, Arthur. Believe what we say or die, seems to be more their present thinking.'

'I think it's good for the King to have control, Merlin, don't you?' Arthur smiled when he said this, and that's when I saw the end from the beginning.

This was the first time Arthur came to Avalon. He received his sovereignty there, and he found his doom there. He would not come again in this life.

Sometimes myths have logical origins. Life is a stage.

In the end, Barley, you have to realise it was all about swords. This new sword gave him something no one else had, an authority no one could challenge. It was not a test of strength, of pulling swords from anvils—such a test could later be challenged. This sword appeared waterborn, from Her. It had to be returned to the Lady of the Lake so there could be no chance of inheritance or the passing on of her authority.

Now I know you could argue that it was trickery, not magic, but the two can be the same. There is much trickery or staging in religion. To a Christian there is no magic, only miracles. I had travelled to find that unique blade and the smith must have put something of himself in his art. The scabbard was pure magic, handcrafted with a healing protective power. It was up to Arthur to wield the sword and instil fear of its power.

Probably in the end rumours about its authenticity would have arisen. Bedivere revered and coveted it. That is why it had to be returned to the Lake at Avalon or Glastonbury.

So there we have it, Barley. How Arthur got Caliburn, which you call Excalibur, which the Saxons believed made him their King, what they called Cyning.

'Hmm,' said Barley, 'I will think on it.'

9

Dancing, Walking and Talking

rthur's first real clear sight of the Tor came as he rounded the foot of Wirral Hill. It rose like a voluptuous breast from the body of the ground itself, a cairn reaching skyward from its highest point. Long ago, in the time of the little people, standing stones had been there but wind and rain and erosion had tumbled them to the base of the hill.

The ancient track meandered around the Tor wrapping itself around the land like a great serpent. Like a labyrinth it was a dancing path. Here the drummers would sound and call the people and then the guiding spirits would begin to emerge. There is only one pathway in and out, and the centre high at the top.

The way is a dance of doubt, a doubt in which we fear to lose our self even though the step pattern is laid out. The labyrinth spiral depicts the way to the unknown centre, the mystery of death and rebirth, the risk of the search, the danger of losing the way, the quest, the finding and the ability to return.

Daedalus the inventor from Minoa, who seemed a genius much like me, created the Labyrinth to hide the Minotaur from the world. The sea people, when they came seeking tin, carved their emblematic labyrinth in the valley of rocks. This was close to the stronghold of Dintagel. It led to the ultimate fear, the dark secret at the centre of life's pathway, which is never straight and may not be as one thought. It was a dance of man and woman, for how could Theseus overcome his fear of death without Ariadne? How could she transform and give birth to new life without him being saving from himself?

Here in the heart of Avalon is where Gwynn ap Nudd, King of the Fairies, keeps his hounds and rides out in the wild hunt to seek souls. Here is where She resides with her dark practices and her sexuality that needs satisfaction. Here is the dark, the lake of remembrance all around under the night sky. Here is a place of power as the wheel turns in the sky. Here could be the straight path of reason and law which yet becomes at every turn a crooked path of craft, art, experience and knowledge found in the pattern of chaos, and with it the fear of getting lost. But here also is opposition to our learned self; a place to find our real self; the pleasure and challenge of exploration; and beneath our dancing feet a ritual conveying the difficulty and the danger of death in seeking our destinies.

This is the way of Avalon.

Naturally Arthur had to climb the Tor, but he found nothing he felt to be of importance. He was never the most spiritual or intuitive of men. He was a gallant soldier, more at home with weapon than pen. His downfall came from those he gathered as his counsellors, young men of physical prowess and little intellect. He did not seek the wisdom of the elders or the wise ways of the veiled sisters. So up there on the Tor he was more interested in the view, to see if he could make out his new base at Carmalet over the moors to the South.

On the summit from the heart of the cairn projected a narrow, slender pillar of stone brought all the way from a sister hilltop in Gaul. Its southern face glistened with a multitude of tiny crystals that shimmered when the sun caught them. The pillar and its shadow formed a sundial by which you could deduce the equinox and the solstice. Around the base were several egg stones which in your time are occasionally found on the Tor as the weather exposes them. Some of these came as a gift from Gaul and some were sent to Avalon from the Valley of the Lady of the Absinth. A dragon path gave an exchange of energy from one power place to another.

I spent time with Morgan on this Tor. As she became more powerful as a queen amongst the mother sisters, we refurbished the sacred grove totems under the direction of the Great Queen spirit. We redecorated the open Hall of the Oracle with scallop shells and used glass shards in four windows, one was blue for water, one orange and red for fire, one brown and ochre for the earth, and one deep blue and yellow for the air. On the beaten earth at the centre we placed the Great Egg stone where she of the Silver Wheel would sit to represent Arianhrod, the thirteenth lady elected by the twelve to serve until her death. In the lee of the hill we placed our sacred bees to make honey for the mead. The oracle would listen to their talking and learn of what they saw and felt.

Morgan and I made this an island of the old ways, for ourselves as much as anything. I could see even on this first visit of Arthur that I would lose him. Morgana and I wanted Beckery to be as it always was—a place of the womb of the earth, sitting low amongst the waters of life, yet up amongst the stars where I was near my kindred. So it was that Morgan in effect made this her palace, a pavilion of wonders and delight. Gwynn became her demon lover like the moon, whilst I, reality in flesh and in my many colours, manoeuvred the puppets. So it was I who placed the carving of the tall bearded man with a solar cross disc on his shoulder, a lamb held to his chest by his left arm and in his right hand a fish and net. For good measure I placed a small crown on his head and a pair of bull horns where his ears should be. Typical horned god of fertility I thought and laughed—how that hateful monk Gildas would love this, my careful prank, my exquisite double entendre!

Morgan still has her place on the mount in your day Barley. She can be found in one precise place and ever will be for those who seek her. The power of any sacred place remains although it fades when desecrated, reinvigorating only when a sympathetic soul attunes to its vibration. It is as ever the power of place which attracts to itself those who can feel its latent emanation and in Morgans' case a pinpoint of where the oracular egg stone lay. It is in such a place the fay will haunt and the sidh ride out.

On the side of the summit I put a small tree trunk carved with three long masculine wizard faces, each with beards and pointed hats. The faces depicted the three phases of mankind. I had owls carved into the wood along with deer and leaves. This was placed near my workshop, where I trained a few local ironworkers in the beauty of bronze. Here we cast a new sacred cauldron with masks and heads around the rim, and in it we placed the images of babes, named for the Mother, both waterborne and star-child.

Although Morgan and her acolyte Nimue loved the place, I thought it windy and it lacked water, which had to be brought up each day from lower down on the other side. That was a chore. Neither was it as comfortable as my place on the Mound. Nonetheless it was a good scheme to show some colour, opulence, luxury and the bounty She provides. Many a good feast and ceremonial banquet was held there on the Tor with good meat and wine imported from the continent.

But today, while Arthur peered around and spoke with the veiled oracle, he seemed more impressed by which beacon fires could be seen from this vantage point. He made sure that the kindling and fuel were dry and under cover. I admired him for this type of attention to detail.

'Arthur,' I said, 'in this land of earth and water you will have to lie one night with a sister in sacred marriage with Avalon, and then you will swear to protect this land.'

'As long as she is pretty,' quipped Arthur—he did not discern the meaning, for he was preoccupied with his own thoughts and hardly listening.

So we left the Tor to look at blowpipes and darts and hear from the little people their knowledge of poisons and how they used these weapons to ambush enemies.

At night, when we were alone on top of the Tor Arthur did however become enamoured of the idea of a star temple and the way the heavens were reflected in the lake. In fact afterwards he had returned to the summit late one evening to see the stars turning overhead, and floating beneath him in the waters. He held his new blade up to the stars and kissed it in the old Sarmatian way. He was profoundly affected by the stillness, the cold, and the feeling of power.

He saw how the Great Bear, a title he held in his name, would turn around the She Bear who in turn would point to the North Star around which the axis of the earth turned and by which mariners found their ways. He noticed how the Dragon looped its way between the Bears in the same way a serpent twines a tree. That night he could almost relate to the gods, but he was fearful of the immensity of the stage above and below. Few men have the magic unless it is transmitted to them by the blood of Lilith.

In the morning he described what he saw as a great tableau and that this should be reflected in Carmalet as a fellowship of warriors of equal status each dedicated as champion to a guardian lady as mistress, harlot or wife each of which together protected the fertility and value of the land in its seasons. He said he would fashion a circular court and not in the Roman way of squares but in the old way of a circle. A true band of equals.

'There is more to kingship than a tumble in the hay,' I told him. 'It is not just the task of bringing harmony and renewal of spirit, nor just bringing purpose to a community whereby the gods may incarnate and provide progress for the people.'

'You mean gold and silver, riches and wealth,' he said. Being a pragmatist I could not bother to explain to this very earth-minded practical man that there was more to life than this.

However, he did tell me about something unusual.

'I saw a young woman that approached me in the night,' Arthur confided in me. 'She rode astride a white horse and talked with me about my ideas. She was very beautiful and said her name was Gwenhwyfa, which meant fair like her hair and smooth like the skin of her breast. I cannot get my tongue around these tribal dialects so I said I would call her Guinevere. She told me her horse was named Epona and that she and the horse were as one. Then she vanished, but I have her fragrance in my mind, the scent of rose and lily of the valley, whose notes assail me all the time. She said she knew my sister Morgan.'

This apparition of his irked me more than a little, for goddesses normally are polite enough to tell me if they step into my territory.

'What a surprise,' I said with a tinge of sarcasm. 'These two do know each other. Your Guinevere is real enough and she is here in Avalon. You shall meet her for sure, by the art and contrivance of your sister I would guess. For the sisters are like Light and Dark, opposites who like a left and right hand work best together. As for the white horse, you as a Roman Briton must know she was the Great Mare. Surely you recognised the name? She was the protector of your ancestors, the cavalry, the draconaria from Sarmatia. She has come to bless you with her protection when you lead against the Saxons.'

'I will be sure to ride a white horse in battle then,' was Arthur's reaction to this spiritual encounter. Down to earth was our Arthur.

Now, Barley, I will introduce you to another character so you can see how matters turned out.

Morgan had a sister called Morgause. She was one of the sisterhood in Arthur's time. Her strength came in midsummer when she took the mantle from Iseult of Ireland, at the time the Holly King arises to defeat the Oak King. This was when the Fairies danced in the long warm nights and the hollow hills resounded with their chanting.

It was said Morgause had elven blood and was possessive like her sister. Perhaps she was more so, for as kindred to Arthur she claimed the crown. She had the beauty of the fire of sunset and so wore a diadem of blood red stone, a carnelian called the setting sun by the people of the pyramids. They said the wearer displayed the receptive or passive female energies and they associated carnelian with the menstrual blood of the mother goddess, Isis. Morgause loved people to know this. She was beautiful, voluptuous and available to men—but on her own terms and for her own gain. She never lost this attraction at any age, and men always fell under her spell. Even when she was grey and her fire had lessened, young men still swooned at the show of her ankle to thigh, at which she was adept.

She married King Lot of Gododdin up in the north. He held territory both south and north of the wall, and his strategic position made him an important ally to Arthur. Her relationship with him gave her some leverage with Arthur and his choices. She quickly bore sons, all ostensibly to Lot, though marriage in the old way was not as the Christians saw it, whereby all power and property passed to the man. Fostering another's son was common amongst the tribes. She gave birth to Gawain who was known for his unparalleled courteousness and his way with women, Agravain, Gaheris and the youngest Gareth. Apart from the youngest, all are now with Arthur as his nephews, helping him build Carmalet.

Arthur wrought his table and made his league of champions. He rode his white horse and married Guinevere. But he chose the wrong pathway.

Anyway Barley, let us go back into dreamtime and meet up with Melwas the local chief, who was older and wiser than Arthur. He had been a vassal to Uther Pendragon and served to protect the sacred temenos of Avalon. He was also warlord of the local tribes—it was one of his men you saw yesterday at the White Spring.

You will be shown that, under the direction of the Lady, Melwas pledged allegiance to Arthur. But Arthur was already pledged to support the Old Path. Come, let us enjoy the moment and you can observe some of the people in dreamtime.

Here, drink this brew of Absinth and Mugwort. It will transport us back in time.

10

The Meeting

I seemed to be floating above a room full of people, looking down on them. I could see myself as a shadow or wraith, like quicksilver neither here nor there; a silvery outline through which I could peer as though I did not exist. I floated down through the ceiling in a realm of my own. I felt Merlin next to me, but I could not see him or touch him; I could only speak to him in my head, and he spoke to me.

'You have accessed your dreamtime, Barley, and one of your ancestors lies below you in the room, hence you could dream backward. Listen, ah you can understand the language now, for you are a long way from home and out of body.'

It was true I could hear and understand every word and as I drifted down I realised that as far as anyone was concerned I was not there.

'You are in Budca, not far from the Tor,' Merlin whispered as though they could hear us. 'That shorter man over there with a grey beard, barbarian style, is Melwas, and this old Roman style building is what I suppose we could call a hunting lodge. At least this is where he stays when he comes up from his base near Cair Guinntguic. You can see from the mosaics that this was once a well-furbished Roman villa. Melwas's realm in these days is a frontline against the invaders, mainly Jutes rather than pure Saxons, so he is a big man for Arthur to keep as an ally.'

Melwas was talking angrily with a younger man.

'You just remember Arthur, apart from swords and Merlin's trickery, you were elected War King and you can be removed whenever we other leaders want to unelect you.   You are right to refortify the old hill forts, I give you that lad, but if you cut timber on my land you ask, and you pay good silver.'

'We need to unite, Melwas, you know that better than I,' replied Arthur. 'Britain needs us together. Between we three—Mark in Kernow controlling the Dumnonii, you the Belgae and myself with the Durorotriges—we hold the West and maintain the war paths to the North. The Cantiaci are all but gone, the Regnenses are hard pressed to hold those South Saxons so the quick sea route to Gaul is lost. In the North the Brigantes have lost half their land and the Iceni and Trinovantes have been slaughtered by the Angles in the East. We need to hold the road system for the cavalry. The forts should let the Saxons pass and then cut off their supplies and their route back after raiding.' Arthur was calm and quiet in tone which seemed to settle Melwas.

'I know all that,' replied Melwas. 'And I also know that the Saxons want silver, slaves, livestock and land in that order. It starts with raids and ends up with invasion. But Arthur, for me to be your man you have to swear to protect our old ways. I am bound by blood to defend this holy place of Avalon. It is protected more than most by marsh and water but if you wish I will temporarily reinforce the Tor without disturbing the High Priestess and the Ladies. I see you have an eye for Guinevere. Take care Arthur, she is May Queen, of budding oak, ash and hawthorn, and may yet have to seed the earth with blood before the Winter Queen Morgana gives up her power.

'She is handsome enough for a young girl but is she fecund enough to bear fruit? She has not yet chosen to be handfasted to any man for a year and a day. But I tell you, this one, she is fickle, flighty and should never have given herself as a holy woman for Avalon. The love of the birds, beasts and provender of the soil is not her concern compared to baubles and the excitement of music and dance for herself alone. Perhaps she was a changeling although she is a beauty.

'I am told she came over from the peninsula of Armorica settled by the southern British tribesmen fleeing the early Saxon raids on the coast. There is a claim she is the daughter of one of Uther's men from a settlement called Kernev. Again, supposedly, she is descended from Conan Meriadoc. He went over to Armorica in Gaul on the orders of the Roman usurper Magnus Maximus with some of his British troops to enforce his claims, then settled them in Armorica. Bit of a mystery woman is our Guinevere.'

'You are quite a historian then, Melwas,' Arthur interrupted him. 'I would like to meet this woman. Will you make an introduction?'

'Is there any real need Arthur? She is the one that has been smiling at you, and you at her, ever since you entered the room. Yes, the same one who has been smoothing her dress to show you how slender and curved her thigh is; the dress with that tantalising side open slit. So no, Arthur, don't take me for a fool—do your own flirting and courting.' Melwas was a bluff and straightforward man. He called out to his bard.

'Melkin, give us a verse or two about a real woman, the one who beat the Romans and burned Londinium.'

'Ah you mean Boudicca, lord. Sure I will, for this very place was named for her when she visited the High Lady for her blessing at Avalon. She came all the way along the Fosse Way to ask for soldiers to join her charioteers in the East to help her spread rebellion. She stayed in this very hall. She was a very great woman, lord, an inspiration to the Britons, and not a drop of Roman blood in her veins.'

Melwas called back,

'You should write these histories and verses down, Melkin, otherwise we will vanish from history like the Druid priests. When they lost their heads we lost everything because everything was in their heads. Write it all down Melkin and history will thank you.' There was laughter.

Suddenly silence fell on the room. In the doorway to the hall stood a tall stately woman with a commanding presence. Her face was serene but severe, her hair black as a raven but streaked with grey, held in heavy braids bound in red ribbon. She wore a deep burgundy gown over which was laid a pure white shawl which sparkled with silver in the light. Her sweet yet sultry fragrance filled the air. This was the Lady Arianhrod, she of the Silver Wheel, High Priestess and ruler of all the ladies. She entered as men and women fell back to let Milady come to Arthur. Some bowed or fell to their knees, and some of the young men just watched her. Either side two attendants swung pottery incense burners giving off clouds of perfumed smoke, but her fragrance did not mingle. It was as though she spoke fragrance—she herself was fragrance.

Merlin whispered that the tall young man on his knees, dour and quiet, was Cai, foster-brother of Arthur.

'He has some magic in him, hence his reverence. He is destined to become one of the Three Enchanted Knights of Britain. Next to him is Bedivere, perhaps Arthur's only truly loyal companion. The ones standing are the Christian warriors,' Merlin whispered. 'You see some are hesitant about kneeling or bowing, while others know where they stand in this power game, calling Milady a witch. But all are in awe; see how they cross themselves—which is superstitious nonsense. But at least all are in awe of her.'

'Come to me now, Arthur,' Arianhrod spoke crisply.

He stood in front of her, eye to eye, each taking the measure of the other.

'Do you not kneel before the Great Mother, boy? Have you come so far to be above us? You cannot be sovereign of the land unless you unite with the Mother. Woman conveys sovereignty, not man. I do not ask you to prostrate yourself or kiss my foot, as did the Roman usurper who calls himself Pontifex Maximus. He took his title from the pagan priesthood, from the Roman gods he so despises. Our brother of Britain, Pelagius, agreed with us that the gods gave us free will. How can you look at your brothers and sisters, as we all are, and call them corrupt in the flesh and sinful. We each have our own capacity to choose for good or ill, as do you. You have a choice today. Those good men from Judea who settled here as followers of the prophet Jesus had no quarrel with us here. Their ten great commandments came from ancient times, from men who were well-acquainted with Astarte. It was Babylon not Rome who first spoke of tablets of stone and simple law.'

She fixed her eye upon a group of warriors among whom a young man called Perceval had spat upon the ground when she entered.

'Some here call me a witch. Well, Arthur, a witch does not engage in gratuitous violence against those who have a different vision, as did the Druids with their bloodlust and their counterparts in Rome today, who purge a soul with torture and burn them to cleanse them of any dissent or heresy. The teachings of the prophet Jesus were brought to Avalon by a family group, who lived a practical life without vows of poverty, chastity and obedience, but their community was overcome by zealots and hermits, who formed their own communities of celibate men. They see us women as challenges to their holiness. Such men seek to own us, use our bodies and steal our status.

'But let me tell you, Arthur, we give ourselves to whom we want. We have authority over our own bodies. Learn this and you will prosper. Do not your Christian men know of some who perform miracles, which I call magic. No, young man, your 'witch' is an invention of those who fear the power of women who worship the seasons and the subtle movement of the waters of the earth. We do not command, but we yield and channel power from the spirits whom you may call angels, whom your book of rules and histories correctly call gods. As well you know Arthur, for you learned from Merlin, the Christos has no power without his bride. So we are at one with all.'

Reaching into an embroidered bag attached to her girdle, she drew out a small platter and cup and held them up in both hands.

'Food and drink; man and woman; pleasure and sensation that satisfies the body, mind and soul. When Yosef, the friend of our people and trader in tin, met our Lady, she gave him a gilded cup and silver platter engraved with the symbols of the hunt and fruits of the earth— something precious to show our values and thank him for his teachings. Yosef's name meant 'Yahweh will add.' Yahweh was a male God, so she teased him by 'adding' to him something feminine, precious, valuable and useful, as is the Goddess, called in his language Shechinah.

'Many years later Yosef returned with his people, friends and family. They were given land and shelter here in Avalon, a place of sacred water and safety. He remembered the symbols of the Great Goddess in Avalon and brought with him these simple olivewood symbols I hold, meaning the simplicity of sharing and the basic needs of we humans. A simple cup and platter of wood can become a Sword and Scabbard, Arthur, sustenance and healing, pleasure in sexuality and the union that can transcend all human thought in ecstasy and rapture.

'We are born through water, as every woman knows, and blood is shed. So it is the great cauldron in which you must be born again of water, Arthur, to be sovereign of this land and to reach the gods.

'So Arthur, do as you will but without harm to others. This is our way here in Avalon, not as those who hide behind the walls as Christian monks. Kiss my ring and see the beauty of the Goddess in its facets, cut by an art Merlin tells me is yet to be discovered. He gave me this graven golden ring and dragon's eye.' She passed the wooden items to one of her handmaidens.

Beside me I felt Merlin's smile of satisfaction and heard his thoughts, 'I wanted to get one step ahead of those rascals in Rome with a prettier amethyst ring cut in brilliant form rather than the Pontiffs old cabochon.'

Arthur reached out and took the Lady's hand, kissing the ring and kneeling on one knee.

'Pass me your sword and belt,' she commanded. He obeyed with difficulty, for he was still kneeling.

'Now kiss the scabbard—for this is woman—then hold it aloft and repeat after me, "For the Gods, Motherland and Honour." '

Arthur did as she said, crying out the words for all to hear. As his voice rang out she took the scabbard and sword and she too cried out.

'Hail Arthur Pendragon, Lord of Britain and Protector of her people.'

The crowd shouted 'Hail Arthur' while in a single gesture she drew the sword and sliced it down toward Arthur's neck—he did not flinch—then rested it his shoulder, then his other shoulder. The onlookers caught unaware gasped and shifted uneasily.

'Arise now, Arthur and lead your people. Tonight conjoin with land and place your sword in the enclosing sacred scabbard.'

People began to cheer and clap, led by Melwas, who called for song, dance and mead. But just as the party began the Lady screamed and went rigid. Two of the priestesses, one I recognised as Morgana, held her up.

'Oh no Morgana not now,' I heard Merlin moan.

The Lady's mouth gaped open, her eyes stared, and deep from within her came the sound of another voice, soft and sultry, like a lovers' drawl, sensuous and beckoning.

'Come my dears, come play you all, let lust rise in your loins and greed within your heart. Go seek for treasures hidden in cup or platter or a cruet for salt and spice. All thirteen will overturn a table, for the dance has begun today and you will dub me in the dance your front to my buttock.'

A light seemed to hover above her. It was difficult to see what it was. Some said it was a round cup, others a precious stone. It shone like the sun and was hard to look at. As it faded she continued.

'What you seek you will never find, for what is not lost cannot be found in another; it is spirit born and expresses itself in visions not reality. You saw a feeling, and what you saw was sacred and whole, but as my cruet is in two, in union and division, so your need is met and the gods empower you in their embrace.

'The dragons rise. Come Smok, fly to me from Wawel Hill! Fly Ladon, from your hilltop Bignor! Red and white, to twine and fight, together or apart—for Pendragon will decide around his solar table. As for Melwas, your dragon with two legs and twining tail will protect this sacred land, unless the water is drained away—then will come flood and tears.'

She stopped talking and shook herself like an animal. Then it seemed she awoke, turned and left without comment.

For a moment all remained quiet. Then Arthur shouted.

'Melwas, where is the feast? It's time to eat, drink, talk and sing.' And so they did.

This was the first time I ever saw real channelling. Sure in Glastonbury I had seen people talk in a meditative state or even trance, and seen folk talk in tongues. But never had I seen an open mouth with a tongue or lips that never moved yet a voice emerged from another world.

'We will return later when the fun begins,' said Merlin.

'What was all that about?' I asked him.

'Time will tell. You will recognise the happenings as they occur, some here and some in your time when you decide to breathe in the scent of she who remembers you, whom you desire in your darkest soul. She will come in a cloud of fragrance and you will then discern the meaning.'

'And what of the wooden items she had from Joseph?' I persisted.

'For them, my dear, you will have to look at the Saxons and to Harold Godwinson's family, the last of the English to win them. Quite another story for another time.'

11

Initiation in the Old Way

The procession spilled down and around the great breast of the Tor, whose outline stood black against the midnight blue sky. Radiant moonlight dampened the stars, leaving only the most brilliant to shine out their message. The cup-bearer of the gods was there, as was the son of Neptune and Medusa who became the thundering horse of Greek Zeus. Near the faint North Star was the King of Aetheopia with his Garnet star glowing red. Midnight blue faded to pale silver blue along the skyline and in the blackness of the mount a ribbon of dancing torches flowed down the sacred way.

We two floated as before, unseen wraiths like mist that has no form.

As the procession dropped from sight only a soft red or yellow glow could be seen like an undulating caterpillar crawling closer over trees and countryside. The first sound of rhythmic thumping could be heard from the procession. A crowd of onlookers waited expectantly around the open dance circle where the daily market was usually held. Around the circle were small turf fires with soft flames that bounced and danced on the expectant crowd's excited faces and warmed the air.

The Guest Lodge lay to the left of the old Roman street. It was built like so many houses of cut and dried turves which would decay and leave not a trace of ever being. Like the people here they would moulder to nothing except good earth. A line of small fires led to the very door of the guest house wherein Arthur was preparing to join in sacred marriage to the Great Mother. The first torches came into view at the top of the rising street.

The crowd stirred and a group of drummers pushed through the throng, echoing the thumping rhythm of the procession as it came winding down the hill. Observing from above, I was enthralled and had quite forgotten Merlin. He spoke now inside my head, 'Look, there I am by the doorway of the Lodge—by the gods I look great!'

Curious I called it, for he was clothed in trews that seemed to be made of leaves, his torso covered with a bright white linen tunic with red embroidery in geometric patterns. On his shoulders lay a cloak seemingly made of bright feathers which glistened and glowed in the increasing light, dancing with many colours, truly a dream coat. On his head was a cap of red fox-skin, its skin and tail hanging loose, crowned by antlers. He held onto a staff although this Merlin was no great age. I concluded that in that getup any Merlin I knew would have keeled over if there were a dance, and the incongruous antlers would fall off.

'I know a thing or two about paper maché and glue you know,' Merlin breathed at me. 'Do you recognise the tune, the rhythm?'

I had felt the rhythm familiar, duhh-duhduhduh-duhh-duhduhduh-duh–duhhduh...then the penny dropped: of course I had heard it before in Cornwall.

The procession stopped, Merlin raised his staff, the drums stopped and the women in the crowd began to ululate and keen for the dead spirits. The peat smoke rose to the sky like ring wraiths and you felt the ancestors creep ever closer as the keening wailed.

Outside the Guest Lodge stood a group of Arthur's young men in Roman garb and armour; more correctly Sarmatian cavalry-style armour suited to Arthur's adoption of the title 'knights' which he was ascribing to his warrior band. I spotted Gawaine and his brothers and

Tristram, who King Mark had sent up from Kernow or, as I say, Cornwall. There were Cai and Bedivere.

'There is Lamorak, the lover taken by Morgause,' Merlin breathed to me.

Some of the women, as though in a trance, started screaming and tearing at their clothes. Others danced provocatively in front of the knights, moving to a chant that the women had turned their keening into. A grey clay painted warrior grabbed one of the women and began to dance as though copulating with her, their hips jerking together. Then from the doorway bizarre figures emerged. They were taller than men, each dressed in sheepskin, white, brown or red. Some had enormous bear-like heads with open mouths and rows of teeth, some had horrible grinning faces and horns like devils, and others wore the heads of goats. Some carried clubs and ran at the crowd, who fell back laughing or screaming.

The drumming and the flute playing renewed with the screech of bagpipes. From the doorway stepped Guinevere, naked except for a kirtle. Oblivious of the crowd, she danced as a person in a trance, her interest centred on a short staff resembling a phallus; it was bedecked with red, black and white ribbons and tipped by a large gourd. She held it up and twirled it as though the universe was at the end of the staff. The crowd seemed to go crazy, shouting and singing a song I could not understand, and from the doorway came the dragon.

The 'dragon' had the stylised head of a horse; its body was a large oval like an upturned canoe with a long tail. The frame was draped in sacking painted with brightly coloured circles and spots, its upper part decorated with coloured ribbons. From the middle of its body projected a man in a grotesque mask of red, white and black, and wearing a long pointed hat. He too was dressed in ribbons and he swung the contraption to and fro as he danced to the music.

Guinevere gyrated in front of the dragon, waving her phallus stick while the bucking and rearing creature chased her. When it was frustrated the effigy ran at the crowd to envelop a woman or a girl who would be lost to sight beneath it as it swayed up and down on top of her.

The air became so sexually charged you could eat the pheromones, the scent of ecstasy filling me as Merlin's hand caressed my ethereal thigh. So we slowly moved with the procession downhill.

'Arthur is in the horse,' said Merlin's mind interacting with mine, 'drunk with shekar from the apple trees. Both he and Guinevere are intoxicated by the incense of mugwort and liberty cap mushroom that filled the guest Lodge, and they have chewed qat, divine food of the ancient Egyptians. They are in another world, in a state of apotheosis. Arthur would dance until he died unless someone stopped him.'

The procession passed Merlin's Mound and on toward the great wheel that was burning high on a pole, its eight spokes turning as their flames were blown by the wind. The kolovrat, the knights called it: an ancient eternal renewing sun symbol of their ancestors.

Arthur, exhausted, was lifted free from the horse. He wanted to vomit, his legs trembled and he felt panic. Soft hands touched him and a soothing voice told him to come to his mother, to dance no more and come to the repose of the earth. Her skin smelled of hay and meadowsweet. He felt he was falling beneath each stroke of her fingers, which smeared sweet oil on his aching limbs. There was the great softness of goose feathers, of the fragile weight of full breasts sliding over his stomach and his chest. His sister's weight came to rest on him, smothering his open mouth as the sweet taste of her saliva joined his. The smoothness of a woman's inner thigh slid over him and he gazed into the depths of the night as his back arched. His manhood pushed into her perilous pathway of unctuous delight, sliding to a state of suspended nothingness the moment her lips let him enter. His life juice spurted upward, inward, before he sighed and relaxed to glorious oblivion. His sister Morgause nodded to the High Priestess and the watching women in the sacred underground chamber, as she eased herself from Arthur's body. In the perfumed smoke from the flickering candles it appears as though the wall paintings moved, writhed and twisted becoming alive and in tune with the rhapsody of elation.

'He is no stallion, but sweet just the same.'

Outside the boisterous crowd had waited. Many were intoxicated by mead, ale and shekar and many had mated without concern as to who their partner was. The High Priestess mounted a dais in front of the now sputtering kolovrat. She raised the phallus with which Guinevere had teased the horse.

'Praise Arthur, the Great Bear of the People, High King of Britain.'

It was Gawain the eldest son of Morgause and Arthur's truest knight who made the first response.

'Hail Arthur, High King of the Britons.'

The next day Ragnell, Dame of Riddles and Gawain's soul partner, confirmed to Arthur the night's events, for in truth he had little recollection. He was still young and had not the self-control or art of full maturity. He was a battle leader.

'My sister?' he shouted. 'I believed it to be Guinevere. You have made me commit a mortal sin.' Arthur had much of the Roman and Christian about him.

Ragnell the wisest and most prudent of the Ladies explained the lineage of the sea peoples whose royalty sought to emulate the gods and goddesses and to set themselves apart from the rest of the population.

'You know this to be true Arthur,' she chided. 'Do not hide behind righteous indignation. Within our compound we are free people to do as we wish, as nature and our personal nature allows. Some are given in marriage, some taken and some free. It is a choice. Your desire was to be High King and it was Morgause, your equal, with whom you lay. For you are not King here in this Avalon but a mere subject to She who turns the Wheel. Lineage comes from the woman, from the distaff not the sword. Your equal, Morgause, will give a royal heir in the old bloodline mixed with your Roman and Sarmatian past—as are many women of this holy temenos. Your son, for it will be a son by her will, shall be called Medraut, he who smites. His number shall be five, the pentacle. He will become King in your absence.'

Arthur was silent.

'I will have Guinevere,' he replied.

'Then she shall be your doom, Arthur the Bear. For Guinevere is no she-bear, she is Queen of the May. And you, my dear boy, are officially a pagan!' Ragnell smiled, then laughed aloud at Arthur's first taste of woman's power.

In the compound of the Christians that night had been set aside for prayer. They prayed for protection from the heathen practices and devil worshipers outside. They laid relics before the altar to protect themselves from the evil influence of the witches. True, many Christians had been in the crowd and the newer Roman brothers had been discussing the penance some would have to suffer when confession would take place. Brother Gildas, a visiting monk well-travelled from Rome and Ireland, had the air of authority. He told the younger monks to ignore the events.

'Arthur is but nothing, an interloper. I am the one with true royal blood; he is just an invention of the demon Merlin and not worth our time. I could save the Britons from the Saxons but I have the Lord's work to do amongst the heathen and the heretics hereabouts. We shall not mention Arthur the traitor to our Lord again, for last night proves the failure of our Lord in this territory of heretics. But we shall not admit to failure. I will write my history of this island, when I am back in Brittany across the sea. This place is sullied by our Celtic brothers who do not admit the supremacy of Rome. They will never be admitted to the saints, except here in this God-forsaken island. Arthur will be forgotten. He will become a mere figment of imagination, an illusion. But my words of Christ will live on.'

A monk called Piran muttered quietly.

'But evidently not forsaken by the Queen of Heaven,' he murmured. 'Some call her Mary, others Mari or even Marzena. She lives on in many strange ways and she herself has wedded Arthur with this land.'

Merlin was talking to me now.

'Arthur is trying to rebuild the citadel, the civitas, at Uirconion, which some call the city of the werewolf. It is a good idea to preserve some sort of administration, but Uirconion is no use defensively—it will fall to the Saxons just as Londinium did, or Eboracum and the tribal capitals of the eastern areas. I am trying to convince him that his best policy is to maintain the hill forts. He needs to make his stronghold here in the West, since the main thrust of the Saxons will come along the valley of the dark river, the Tamesas. That valley is the soft underbelly of the South. He who holds the Tamesas and the River Sabrina holds the South and West.'

'Why is Uirconion called werewolf?' I interjected.

'From the Thracian cavalry stationed there I guess. They are from your modern-day Bulgaria – always big on werewolves round those parts. And before you ask, in your time the city is called Wroxeter. How the mighty have fallen! Uirconion was once a very fine and rich Roman town rivalling Londinium, and even now is still a thriving hub on the River Sabrina easily reached from here upriver. So Arthur needs to build his string of forts and hold all the northern tribes west of the mountain spine of the Pennines and up as far as Rheged. Having Uirconium as an administrative centre, a judicial court with all the trappings of Rome, does make sense—and it has everything a Roman Briton could want, from bathhouse to basilica and Christian churches—but the tribes are wary of it. The petty kings can only be held in check by Arthur's legion and heavy cavalry. So he needs his back stop, his castle at Camelot as you call it.'

Merlin explained more about Arthur's strategy.

'The idea of a circular tableau of young men, each equal in status, was conceived by the circle of the land here in Avalon, and the cycle of the seasons. You saw this on the same magical night as he met Gwenhwyfa. Each knight must unite with the woman as his goddess, seeking her favour and empowering her. These young men, from peasant to king's sons are inspired by the idea of a greater Britain, the goddess Britannia, that ancient Lady of the symbol of fire and water.

'Arthur needs the tribal people to love him independently, and the only way he can get that love and loyalty is from the goddesses and gods of the countryside. Hence the sponsorship of She of the Silver Wheel who commands many waters. Swords have always been blessed by water, and I made sure Arthur has not only a forged sword but one clearly given from water.'

'But that was a trick, it wasn't real!' I rounded on him.

'So are you saying I am not a spirit? Are you saying that a miracle must never be something contrived? All ceremony is contrived. It is theatre. Belief does not simply mean what is in accordance with fact or reality. As the Christian prophet asked, 'What is actually truth?'

'Enough Barley. Come and see the young men ride North toward Rheged. Morgan is assigned by our Lady to ride with Arthur as her representative, to keep him in check and to keep the Christian bishops from interfering and taking too much land for their churches. In particular the right of free women to trade and own land must be maintained. Marriage should require no religious ceremony, but only be a mutual agreement to live together in harmony. It should not be the subjugation of a woman to a husband who takes all her rights away. That is a Christian idea. Morgan is of royal blood and connected with the tribes of the North as a Cornovii, as priestess, royalty and sister to Arthur. We can expect a cat and dog fight.

'They will fight their first major pitched battle against the Eastern Angles and Bernician settlers by supporting King Artuis of the Pennines. They will fight by the river Glein to drive a wedge between the Angles and Bernicians and reinforce Pons Aelius as a Brigantes tribal stronghold. Come and see them ride out.'

It wasn't quite like the films of today, neither scruffy axe-wielding barbarians, or shiny medieval knights. The armour was mainly leather or scaled with metal plates. The helmets burnished metal, some with horsehair plumes. Many carried long heavy lances from which danced dragon pennons. Round shields carried many different emblems, some Celtic, others geometric tamgas. Some had flags attached to their backs flapping like wings and most had stirrups which of course they needed to compensate for the heavy lances. These were the Sarmatian styles Merlin had told me about and described. The mounted archers had no stirrups which was the norm for these times and they carried curved short bows, rounded basketwork shields so as to be light and fast moving. Behind them trotted a column of tribesmen, some painted in grey clay, others painted with blue designs like tattoos, most carrying bows and axes. Then there was Morganna, riding like a queen. And next to her Nimue, dressed in green and carrying her great bow, for she was an archer, with her small warband of women with their amazon shields.

I was glad I had seen this parade, for however academics decry it now, it was romantic. It was a special time, when hopes were high and more harmony of purpose existed. John Duncan captured it so well in his painting The Riders of the Sidhe.

Arriving back on the Mound with a start I eagerly questioned Merlin.

'What happened to Guinevere? All the old stories tell of her love and marriage to Arthur.'

Merlin spat and scratched his head.

'It's a long story, Barley, and such journeys we have undertaken take a toll on my energy. The essence is this. Guinevere ran after Arthur and his war band. She stole one of the sacred white horses, left her position as one of the Ladies, for she wanted to be High Queen. Arthur married her in the Christian way partly in revenge for the trick played upon him with Morgause. Melwas, who was with Arthur, took Guinevere back to the Lady of the Lake. But she was married in Christian fashion, so it was said she was abducted and kidnapped. Melwas was only doing his duty. Some of the band led by Lancelot were sent back to retrieve Guinevere and a fight developed. Because of this Arthur was weakened, so his first battle in the North was not conclusive. The breach between Melwas and Arthur never healed.

'Guinevere was always a flighty piece and had no idea of what being a Christian meant. She took up with a variety of lovers, not realising that authority over her body now rightfully belonged to Arthur, along with all her property. Lancelot was just like her, handsome, self-admiring, daring, and with no respect for the feelings of others. He had been foster child of the Lady of the Lake across the water in the Armorican peninsula, where many Britons had settled over the years. I say Lake, but over there it was the Lady of the Fountains. Guinevere's affair with Lancelot, however, went too open and too far. It showed the Christian population that Arthur accepted sin. Lancelot rescued her from being burned alive for her infidelity, killing several of Arthur's best men. She ended up as lover to Arthur's son when he took the throne, then she was again a Queen. When both Arthur and his son were killed in the final battle she became a nun and founded a religious community. There will soon be a Christian community of women on Arianhrod's island, by her permission as descendant of Guinevere's repentant self-pity. Her acolytes returned her body here to the Lady of the Lake according to Guinevere's wishes.

'That's it for today Barley, enough potted history.'

12

To Be a Water Maiden

Orla and I were becoming friends. We struggled with language, but found our way to a half-language of our own. We each thought the other strange, for after all in reality we were centuries apart. But we were both women and had the same attitude toward spiritual values, medicine and practical matters. What appealed to me most was the contentment she seemed to have.

So I came to learn the way herbs should be gathered and dried, powdered and preserved. I learned about the healing oils that could be milled from seeds and used instead of animal fats and olive oil. I learned how the energy of the plant could transfer its power, communicating its value. In turn I tried to explain the complexity of the cell and how science was confirming her work. But she had no time for this.

'I have no need to know how it works,' Orla told me. 'I work with experience. Each person has their own need, and when I touch a person I feel their need—I listen with my hands.'

She taught me to massage. Her hands moved to take me from the lightest feather touch to the deepest pressure, but never pain. Orla despised pain except in a crisis. She used her forearms in sweeping strokes which gave me pleasure. There was no sexuality, just pleasure as I purred like a cat and relaxed to a level I had not experienced since I was a babe in arms.

Orla showed me how to heal animals by touch alone, and how to care for horses. In fact I learned to massage a horse before I was allowed to massage another person. It was when the horse snorted and moved against me that I realised more than massage was happening. When a big powerful horse gave me its hoof and leg to 'comfort' I realised there was more to touch than rhythm and a pattern of disciplined strokes. Only when I felt the hard muscles of a horse turn to softness did I realise there was communication beyond understanding. Only then did Orla let me touch others for healing.

Peterkin Thumblesticks taught me the art of hand projection. I had experienced that my hands felt hot when I laid them upon a person. Peterkin explained that the flow of goodlife, as he called energy or spirit, could be projected at some distance. He explained that for most people the circuit of power let my left hand receive and my right hand transmit. I found I could feel a soft cloud of energy like cotton wool or finest down between my hands, and feel this cloud above the skin of a person.

But I wanted more than this. I wanted to confront the goddess, and feel her as part of me. I wanted to be whole, at oneness with what I could not understand. The land of Avalon beckoned me. I wanted to be identified in myself with one of these ladies, to be a priestess, a goddess within myself, for myself.

So early one morning Orla and I took a coracle and paddled through the reeds and water out toward the old lake villages. There had been much Roman work here reclaiming land, but we headed to a quiet place. We passed two swans, which Orla said was a good omen, and entered a place of treacherous stagnant water densely covered in duckweed. Trees rose from the water, their fallen branches covered in moss flung to the water to decay into black arms clawing from the grassy peat. In the distance a woodpecker drummed.

'I will wait for you here', Orla said. 'Push onward and you will come to a grove of alders. Find what you will there. You will feel beneath your feet a buried trackway. Follow it to the grove. Take your time, it is no more than fifty yards. See the trees towering up over there, it's not so far.'

I took a half-rotten stick and stepped onto the bank where the coracle had touched. I sank into the black ooze but Orla gestured for me to go onward. The green water was cold, really cold, but I felt beneath my feet a surface, which my toes told me was like some basket or wattle work. Easing each foot forward, I slowly felt for the hidden path as my clothing dragged in the clinging water and weed. Then quickly there was a rise, the ground soft but not water-logged. I was surrounded by trees growing closely—many with two or three trunks—black fissured bark glowering into the sky with the ground littered by twigs and tiny black cones. Fallen leaves covered retreating oxlips, wood anemones and the feathery foliage of corydalis.

These alder trees belonged to Bran or Brian the Blessed, symbols of death and resurrection. Merlin had asked me, 'What can no house ever contain? Answer: the piles upon which it is built.' Resistance to water and rot made this a tree for Avalon, and the old lake villages were founded upon it.

I could see the dark fae, fairies of the alder, flitting high above my head watching me. When these fairies leave the alder they take on the guise of ravens, the birds who protect great Bran. Today I felt they were protecting me—just as alder wood became shields for warriors, the fae were shielding me from harm.

Orla had told me that when cut the tree oozed red dye, and its spring leaves and flowers gave a green dye used to camouflage hunters and to colour the green clothes worn by fae people. But why was I here?

I walked toward some reed grass growing from a pool of clear water. The water bubbled from a spring and trickled in a tiny rivulet away into the moss-covered peat. I knelt on the moist earth, dipped my cupped hand into the water and drank, letting water splash back into the pool, disturbing the stillness. Suddenly my hand was grasped and pulled into the water. Screaming in terror I was tugged down from the bank. As my face and head disappeared underwater my screams gurgled from my open mouth. A laughing face looked straight into mine. It was a beautiful woman's face, decorated with make-up as though in the open air. She pulled me down further and I swallowed water instead of air and felt myself slipping away from physical life. In blind panic I thrashed, seeing light above me yet being pulled further downward. Suddenly she let go and my hands reached up to grab at grass, reeds, anything to get me back on the bank. As I crawled choking onto the land I lost my balance and slipped again back into the water. My feet found no bottom. I grabbed wildly at the grass tussocks, but they came away in the hands. Then she held me and lifted me onto the bank. She swam and moved like a fish.

'So, my dear, you are reborn by water. You tasted death and resisted it, and now you have come to the point of rebirth and change. Be calm and have no fear, for this is why you came. Between life and death is a delicate line.'

'Who are you?' I gasped.

'Some call me Calypso, but hereabouts I am named Clethrad the alder nymph. Others just call me Rusalka, but you may call me Barley, for I am like you. I am the fierce one you hide, who holds your darkest secrets and desires, from whom you struggle to be free, yet keep just the same. I am the being buried deep within you, beneath your morality and conscience, who wants to escape.'

She pushed me to the bank and I crawled out of the water. I turned around and peered into the pool, but she was gone. I saw only my own face reflected back, pale, frightened and tearful. I touched my clothes and found they were dry. My skin was dry, my hair was dry. The face in the pool, my face, smiled at me and blew a bubble toward me like a kiss. I shuddered, scared for a moment, but a soft sound of pipes sung into my being. I felt sick and retched and spat water and pondweed. I had been in the water and she had given me life, and I had given myself license to be my true self without guilt, But which face was mine—this one or the painted beauty?

A strong scent came to me. Merlin had taught me that the gods came with fragrance and were in essence fragrance. I had asked Orla to let me be the goddess, to take me as her worshiper and acolyte. I wanted her to recognise me as her servant, her instrument. Was she here? I looked around and saw no one. I closed my eyes yet still I heard the pipe music. All my senses were alert now. Every nerve sensed something. The darkest and the oldest alder tree sighed in the wind and seemed to look disapprovingly, as though the bark spoke, but I knew this was the light playing tricks. Then I remembered Merlin and his tricky ways. So I looked more closely at the fallen leaves piled around the branches and there he was—a masked man with blue eyes lying among the leaves.

Masked I say, but he was but a heap of brown and russet leaves. On his head was a wreath of fallen leaves and bare twigs.

'Do you not know me?' He asked. 'I was your Jack. I was Jack in the Green, but even now I am the spirit of the apple trees, the Green Man, Robin Goodfellow or Robin of the Hood. What name do you prefer?'

I walked toward the man. He seemed to stir but when I got there I saw it was an illusion, a trick of light. I kicked angrily at the leaves. What I had thought to be a resting arm was no more than a broken, time-blackened rotting branch. Was I going mad? What voices was I hearing? Perhaps my near-drowning had shocked me, and this detachment from reality was what a doctor would call shock.

'Breathe,' I said to myself out loud, 'sit.'

So I sat on the damp moss, and silently opened my palms to the sky. I could hear everything: the bubbling water, birds twittering far away, the distant lowing of cattle. The breeze rustled and things moved—I heard them all.

I had been in the water for sure. A water nymph or sprite had pulled me down but brought me back, like a resurrection or even a baptism. I had heard water spirits are always present where dark alders grow and white willow waves to the sun. But what of the scent I had smelled so strongly?

I closed my eyes and tried to concentrate on any scents my nose could smell, but nothing came. I tried to remember what Orla had said about her ancestry. Some generations ago her people were slaved from Egypt and sold into Scythia. As time passed her grandmothers found freedom and migrated with the Romans to Gaul, where her immediate grandmother was captured and taken as slave to Ireland. From there her mother had escaped to Avalon. The traditions of Egypt still clung to her, passed from mother to daughter. She related the Ladies of these Roman Britons to more ancient beings, some of whom I was familiar with. Their names rung down through centuries: Isis, Hathor, Nut, Sekhmet and the trilogy of Memphis namely Ptah, Sekhmet and the divine son Nefertum.

Orla had explained, as had Merlin, that the nose leads us to the gods and goddesses. Through offerings of sacred perfumed smoke we could see the gods. Indeed, she had said, the Egyptian temple was laid out like the nose and its chambers. The cult of Isis was still strong in Britain, she claimed, and her family were of the older ways of Memphis.

It had not occurred to me until this moment that Ptah the Creator god, was always painted green! 'Ptah conceives the world by the thought of his heart and gives life through the magic of his Word'.

This was what Merlin had written, or so he said, in Wikipedia. Ptah was the god from whom all flora and fauna arose, like the virility of the green man that has forever lived in the woods of Albion. Sekhmet was Ptah's sister and wife, being daughter of the sun god Ra—Her name meant Powerful One but she was nicknamed Nesert, meaning flame, and the eternal flame of the sun was her crowning symbol. A flame was always lit in her temples, wafting scent from the fragrant oil lamp.

I was thinking of Nefertum when I first felt a twinge of excitement that I had made a connection with some hidden knowledge just out of reach. Something was happening in my logic and reason, brought on by a cause I could not identify. Nefertum was the divine son of Ptah and Sekhmet; his symbol was the blue lotus that rose from the water at sunrise. It revealed the blue of the sky with the yellow centre of the sun, but above all it gave the intoxicating perfume of the gods. This addictive fragrance filled the mind with its beauty, satisfying the body and satiating the soul. Nefertum was the god of perfume and aromatherapy, cosmetics and healing, the god of the rose, geranium and cornflower, the god of surrender.

Had that fragrance, that song and music, come from the water nymph, from the primeval deep to which all water still flows? Orla always said that fragrance either evokes or provokes, and I had been affected by that smell: there was no doubt about it. What had it reminded me of? Was she still there in the water?

I caught sight of a jay flitting amongst the branches, revealed by its distinctive white rump and creaking screech. It looked at me and fluffed its pinkish brown feathers and blue flash whilst staring through its black moustache. Screeching again it flew out of sight—I guessed to Merlin, unless indeed it was Merlin. The bird's almost magical presence, for jays are shy birds, gave me more confidence. I returned to the silent pool and saw my reflection looking normal. I smiled and saw myself smile back. The pool was bigger than I had thought. What I had thought to be firm ground I now saw was floating, quaking peat moss, and the pool extended beyond what I had thought was its boundary.

Gingerly, with my staff prodding forward to test the ground, I walked further. The ground trembled beneath me as I went forward. The pool, fed by a spring, which accounted for the bubbles I had seen, was on slightly raised ground, which accounted for the rill of the out-flow. A rippling circle of wavelets came from one side and I pulled back from the edge, as I did not want to see Rusalka again. Then I saw a fin rise above the water and realised it must be a fish, perhaps a trout or even a salmon—for they came upriver along with the eels in season. The jay screeched again. Like a flash the phrase 'salmon of wisdom' sprang to my mind. Here in the alder grove I had found a protective water sprite, a large fish, and seen dark fairies. This grove was proving to be a place of in-spirit-ation! I played with the word. And then that fragrance returned, sweet like the dusky scent of hon-eycomb overlaid with the tang of fresh orange peel. I felt rather than smelled it, as though it was a taste that made me salivate. And here too came a penetrating, smooth and rich aroma which I felt was exot-ically elegant yet reminiscent of dry tea, spices and a floral note; yet full-bodied, spicy and wine-like. It lifted me to a feeling of swooning or swimming. I let my arms rise and twist in an indiscernible rhythm, my wrists turning and fingers playing like an Eastern houri. My breasts swayed and my nipples enlarged with a satisfying fullness of sensa-tional delight. As the flower scents fled and faded from my being I was overwhelmed by a sense of power coming into my belly, no longer taking me high to the clouds but bringing me to earth, like a deep cream of intensity. I breathed it all in, slowly taking the fragrance deep into my soul as it dominated and overtook my body, which trembled as though drugged with milkwood. Now I was bewitched by a soft odour of vanilla with cognac, oakwood barrels, warm, animalistic, earthy and mesmerising. How could I describe such feelings? There were no words, for I knew She had come.

From the water a mist rose, and above it a striking woman with ash blonde hair seemed to hover. She wore a shift of red and a midnight blue cape, edged with golden beads that seemed to dance along the seams and hover around her shoulders. On her right wrist was a blood-red band and her arms bore blue spiral tattoos. She held before her a blade, which glinted like the sun, looking like a flame. I was dazzled and speechless.

'I am Elaine,' she said, lowering the sword to her side. 'You will become mine in your time. Feel me in you now. Feel my strength to obtain my desire with deception and guile. You will love words and become a smith of poetry as well as iron, for words may strike a blow harder than steel. I hold the grail you have seen, in which the milk of substance may be spewed. You will control the plunging of the blade so no man will take you, except you freely give. You will yearn for the beloved, but it will always be beyond your reach. Remember where I found you. Now go, for you have what you desired. But if you do not bend to my will I will break you, for today I have shown you fear and the end of life.'

I felt suddenly cold. I hastened back to find Orla, who had set a fire and was grilling fish.

'Did you hear us, Orla?' I asked.

'I heard the singing of the trees, the chorus of woodland birds, the rustling of leaves and splashing of waterfowl. What else is there to hear in this lonely place? I like the band on your wrist,' she added. I had not noticed the red band.

A swan glided silently from the reeds.

13

Holy Ground

Merlin would have the answer to Barley's burning question. 'Who was Elaine in the pantheon of Goddesses?' But Merlin was playing hard to get.

'Oh my goodness, Barley, just let me get on, I have work to do.'

Barley pulled a face.

'Merlin, I was nearly drowned. I am still not right, upset I suppose, and I don't know where I am and my mind is disturbing me. I haven't slept well. I can't separate reality from fiction anymore. Frankly I'm frightened of my own thoughts, of spirits taking me over. I don't know who I am any more.'

Merlin's face softened.

'I am so sorry Barley. Be sure, you are who you are right now, present on the ground with me. If I poke you, you hurt. That's reality. However, when you sleep you dream, and although you are still real your mind takes you to weird places and you see people you don't know but feel you do. Many things that are not real happen in dreams. You are there sleeping on the bed, quite real, but in your head you are in another world.

'I talked about this before, but let me explain more fully. You have ancestors, and you have characteristics from those ancestors, male and female. Those characteristics could be physical or mental. Some of your ancestors had mundane lives, others had interesting or even game-changing lives. Their characteristics live on in you, and you manifest them to all who see or know you. You hear this all the time from older people: such and such a child is just like her grandmother or even great aunt.

'We go on journeys or retreats to seek ourselves, because sometimes we are so like someone who has gone before that we need to find ourself. We have to live this life that constrains us, our work and children and so on, but some of us feel we are missing something within. This feeling increases as we get older; we may pass a stranger in the street yet feel we know them. A man may smile at you, and you respond, because he is familiar although you never met him. You might keep seeing the same person, perhaps on the same path or in same shop, as though this day is important. The coincidence is too much. So many strange feelings come to us, Barley. Yet rarely do we stop to say, "I'm sure I know you," or to ask if we have met—it would sound too much like a chat-up line and just isn't done.

'Memory is a strange thing. You will not find it in the brain in one place like a filing cabinet. It is partially held outside us, like an electrical field. Which means we can bump into another person's memory if it matches, if there was a previous connection, perhaps with an ancestor, for memory can be passed on. It's a bit like hysteria that catches like a force-field of panic.

'Did you hear about that man who remembers the film Knickerbocker Holiday scene by scene but never saw it? His mother saw it when he was in her womb. The film featured the September Song, which reduces him to jelly even today. So she conveyed her emotion to him and he remembers!

'I have seen your ancestors and you have a common trait of being drawn to spirits, to another world where you reach out to break free from the constraints of your world. You are a free spirit. No doubt in the distant past your ancestors consorted with the spirit gods like the fabled Tuatha de Danaan.

'I have told you that smell and memory are bound together, that memory reacts to smell. It is the first sense you develop in the womb. Our sense of memory is so quick that we hardly notice it. But you do notice the vibrato of familiarity it picks up across a crowded room. When you catch a familiar or exciting eye you experience a shared knowing beyond your immediate grasp. That man or woman coming toward you holding your eye is your shared past recognising oneness.

'Look in your Bible. When Mary of Magdala saw Jesus in the garden she did not recognise him, she thought he was the gardener, until he spoke her name. Other disciples recognised his characteristics, not his appearance. He walked along a road with two of his disciples, who did not recognise him until he had a meal with them. It was the inherent characteristics of his spirit ancestry that marked him out. It's the same today, the fae recognise the fae.

'So all we are doing on our travels together is looking deep within your memory, your dreamtime. Sometimes it feels like a dream, such as when we float outside reality looking down on Arthur and Melwas; at other times we inhabit our ancestor's mind, being there in our mind's eye, remembering.'

Merlin handed Barley a vial of scent.

'Here, breathe this in. No don't sniff it; let it come to you, gently breathe it in. Put a drop on your wrists and rub them together, now smell your wrist, see how the warmth changes the aroma. Put some at the back of your neck. When you want to evoke the past or invoke a spirit in ceremony you should put this scent as an offering on the soles of your feet, the base of your spine, behind your knees, on your solar plexus, the back of your neck and wrists. You will become a cloud of scent; an offering of yourself ascends in a cloud that draws down the specific god or goddess.'

Barley smelled the freshness again, the scent of marshland, of farmyards and rosemary. There was peat smoke and the aroma of freshly cut wood, but it was all sweet like an overpowering perfume in a bottle that invaded her.

Not put off by this interlude, Barley collared Merlin the moment they got back to the Mound.

'Right then, off we go up to the Christian Quarter,' he barked at her. 'It's time you got to grips with your pagan calling versus your Christian upbringing of sorts.'

'What's got into you?' she cried. 'You were always wary of that part of Avalon, but you have nothing to fear from decent Christian folk.'

'That may be true my dear, but sarcasm does not become you,' he responded. 'It will not be long before the likes of you will be stripped naked while some seedy man hunts for a Devil's mark or a third nipple; or before some kid you annoyed tells the priest your cat is a devil and you stopped the cows from giving milk; then you could end up on a bonfire. So, madam, don't get too cocky just because all you have to fear from religion in your day is a superstitious, woman-hating prophet blowing you up on a plane!'

This outburst silenced Barley for the rest of their walk up the hill. They crossed the busy market and entered the Christian quarter lying before the compound proper. There was the little church of fable and myth just as described. It was quite a large building but basically was made from upright logs between which were walls of thick mud layered over vertical wattle hurdles. The roof was reed thatched with a small cross placed at the gable end. There was a small bell tower in front of the church and a wellhead to one side. People were going about their business and the usual scrabble of chickens and children were running about.

The inside was plain and scrupulously clean, with a plain altar and wooden cross. There was a big heavy curtain to one side that could be pulled across to screen the altar. Light came from the under eaves windows, some of which had coloured glass giving a jewelled appearance to the walls as light played through the windows.

'My work,' Merlin observed. 'Pretty isn't it? This church is now dedicated to Mary but which one is in question. Originally it was a simple meeting room with two compartments, a bit like the Jewish tabernacle.'

Benches lined the wall leaving the centre free for people to stand. The ground was covered by freshly-strewn herbs that gave off the sweet odour of chamomile. It was a pleasant refreshing place of calm and piety.

'Look over there,' Merlin nudged Barley to look at a painted board standing to one side like a large Russian icon. It was of a woman with a dark complexion, her head framed by a golden solar disc adorned with twelve stars. She wore a crown. It was very old and the paintwork was darkened by the smoke of an oil lamp lit in front of her.

'Any comment?' Merlin asked.

'Looks like an old Russian icon of Sophia or even an earlier Minerva,' Barley commented after thinking through the iconography of the symbols.

'Not bad,' Merlin responded. 'But think of your schooldays and religious instruction lessons. The gospel book of Luke, a doctor by the way, recorded that when the women went to the tomb after the death of Jesus they found it empty. The women were recorded as Mary Magdalene, Ioanna and Mary the mother of James. Now suddenly this Joanna appears, out of the blue. But Barley, Io was a moon and water goddess of Egypt and once her queen; and in Aramaic Anna means goddess. So take out a comma and you arrive at Mary Magdalene Queen and Goddess.

'Interesting, but let's continue. Luke tells us these women prepared fragrant spices, ointments and spices. Luke had already told us of the 'sinner' who cleansed the feet of Jesus with her tears and dried them with her hair, who then proceeded to tenderly kiss his feet and massage them with perfumed oil from an alabaster jar—a very sensuous action, Barley.

'The Bible is full of tricks, innuendo and hidden meanings. I can tell you that Luke was waxing allegorically here. He had already written, 'The Queen of the South will rise at the judgment with the people of this generation and judge them, because she came from the ends of the earth to listen to the Wisdom of Solomon—and see, something greater than Solomon is here!

'Now, one of the great love poems is found in the Bible, the Song of Solomon. It was a prophecy in effect about the Christ and about the woman in the song. The poet said, "Where has your beloved gone? My beloved has gone down to his garden, to the beds of spices." This southern woman was thought to be the Queen of Sheba. The song records, "Do not gaze at me, for I am dark because the sun has touched me." And there you have it in a nutshell, Barley: a Black Madonna. The Magdalene, illicit lover or partner of Jesus, demonised by the Roman Church as a prostitute—but not, by the way, by the Orthodox Church. And what of the beloved in the Song? Well, he is wisdom personified, yet in a feminine form. A bit transgender isn't it? And all that, Barley, is staring you in the face here in Avalon.'

The door opened and a monk came in. It was clear the man was a monk only by his head being partly shaved.

'Come now Merlin, you know father Gildas does not like you here.'

'And what would you do, Brother Cadfan, without the medicines I help you 'invent'? Anyway I have someone wanting to know more of the church history here. Why don't you tell a little of it?'

'We would be here for hours, Merlin, and I would be called away. But let me try to summarise matters, madam. As everyone knows some of the Holy Family settled here, and that would be about thirty years after Our Lord's death. History records that this group included Joseph the uncle of Jesus, and under Talmudic or Jewish law the protector of his brother's wife Mary. The local king gave them some land because Joseph was well known locally for his trade relations as a metal merchant. They lived here peacefully for many years as a family unit with their Jewish traditions. Many of the locals fancied the ideas these Christians put forward. In fact early Christianity hereabouts came from traders and travellers, not missionaries like Paul, bless his soul.

'Eventually two emissaries of the true church arrived and organised the community of Christians, setting up moral codes, promoting use of the memoirs or gospels of Christ's disciples as inspired sacred texts, and appointing elders and deacons. The letters of Paul were circulated within the community and became their doctrine and law. The authority of the Church in doctrinal matters was ordered by the Bishop in Londinium, so a number of things were regularised. The Sabbath was changed from the Jewish Saturday to Sunday as more appropriate, and Easter was separated from the Jewish Passover Meal. Moreover people had to be reminded it was the Jews who murdered the Christ.'

'I thought it was the Romans who killed your Jesus,' interrupted Merlin, adding ingenuously, 'Am I right in saying it was this same Paul that relegated women to a secondary role in your religious life?'

'Of course. He instructed that women have no special role in Christian culture except as good wives who obey their husbands. He did not permit a woman to teach any law or doctrine, for it was a woman who tempted man and brought death to the earth.

'Anyway, Christianity grew amongst working people in urban society, and here too in Avalon, but there was no conflict until after the persecution of Christians by the emperor Diocletian. Then came Constantine the Great, who learned his Christianity from his mother who was taught in Britain. When he made Christianity the state religion, many upper class Britons converted to the ways of the Lord.'

'But how come there are so many monks here?' Barley asked.

'Good question,' said Cadfan. 'I suppose it is because men and some women wanted to be perfect, without sin. Indeed, Our Lord said we should be no part of the world. So they went into the desert to resist temptation, as Our Lord had done. But that didn't work out well in the desert. So hermits spread out to find more favourable places. Some arrived here in Avalon, which was away from the beaten track and had been a Holy Christian place since early times. They set up small cells and gradually started helping each other until formal groups began to emerge. Eventually they formed a compound within the temenos of the Old Church, but away from the common community. That is what you have today in effect.' Cadfan glanced over his shoulder as though he was about to share a secret—perhaps he was frightened of his next words being overheard.

'Of course, I accept the hermit called Collen did not help Christianity in Avalon, for he became an early sort of abbot and father to the monks. He tried to stamp out local beliefs and confined the priestly women to the island by force. He poisoned the local chieftain when he went for a meal with him, by getting him and his retainers to drink what he called holy water. These days we look back and call it a miracle, for he banished the king of the fairies. But I know the truth, because I write things down—I am scribe here, second only to the Abbot. I have the writings of Phagan and Deruvian who brought the canon of the scriptures here and the teachings of the Christian Council.

'More time passed, and it came about that a young man called Patricius, from a wealthy Christian family, was kidnapped by Irish pirates from the coast near here. He spent some years enslaved as a shepherd in Ireland. He eventually escaped and returned home, but then he went back across the sea to convert the Irish to Christianity. After Patricius completed his missionary work in Ireland he retired

129

here to Avalon (which by the way I prefer to call Ynis Witrin). He became the first Abbot here in our monastery. In fact you can see his grave over there clearly marked.

'There had always been a college of twelve monks here, but Patricius felt the need for a regular father or Abbot. He decided we should all dwell together, eat and drink in common and sleep in the same house. He set the rules of this house we follow to this day, giving reverence to the Holy See of Rome.

'You will see some monks here who subscribe to the old Celtic ways, closer to the old Jewish customs. But these heretics are slowly being pushed aside.'

Cadfan fell silent as Merlin thanked him and turned to Barley.

'I hope you got the story, Barley. Did you notice how Jesus's teachings moved from honest men and women to a hierarchy of despots in just a few years? The Oligarch cannot stand freedom, I tell you.'

'Is Brigid around somewhere, Cadfan?' Merlin asked.

'Yes she is, over by the farm toward the sick house. But she is in no mood for your nonsense after having a row with Gildas. He just does not get on with women, especially the Irish. He says they should all move near you. God help you if they land on your doorstep. Now shoo, or I shall have to explain why you were here at all.'

'You mean Bridget the saint, the one from Kildare,' gasped Barley as they strode along the street from the market.

'Who else! And you can ask her all about Elaine, for she and Arianhrod are like two peas in a pod. It's difficult sorting out the male saints as to which god they actually have taken over, but women are a lot easier to trace.'

A small group of men headed them off, all monks and mostly holding up crosses.

'I told you before, Merlin, don't come here,' the oldest one warned. 'And don't bring your tarts either.'

'Just bog off, Gildas, or I shall turn you into a frog and then you can croak even more. It's still a free country, this Britain of ours, at least until you shackle us to Rome again. Maybe the Saxons have a point and Arthur will keep us out of your Un-Holy Empire!'

'Take your poxy doxy and scram!' was all Gildas could shout in reply.

Barley saw red. She stopped dead and fixed her eye on Gildas.

'I am the maiden when first I come to you, for I put on a modest face and speak chaste words. But you know beneath the hem of my shift I am a pillar of fire to consume you in unholy embrace. Be gone you milksop whelps.'

With that the men turned, hitched up their robes and scurried off.

'Well done girl, I see Elaine has had an effect,' Merlin laughed.

A woman was milking a cow in the bothy. She was buxom with chestnut hair escaping from her bonnet, wore a green shift and an overdress of brown. She was dressed without finery, but the linen and wool was of fine quality. She was singing as she worked and had not heard their approach.

'Now there is a fine figure of a woman, to be sure,' Merlin said, with a twinge of an accent that Barley recognised as the lilt of the Irish.

'Humbug!' the woman retorted. 'Go away—you pagans make the milk turn sour.'

'Which surely is enough for you to know, Brigid, that must then be a miracle which even the Holy Father in Rome would recognise as something of a special power coming from a god.'

'Och get away from me you old reprobate.'

They continued to banter for a while until she had finished milking, whereupon she dipped a cup and offered it to us.

'I hear the monks want to move you and your novices from off the main island to a place of seclusion more suited to your woman's temperament,' Merlin idly spoke to the air.

'You will not provoke me today, Merlin, for I have spoken with Arianhrod and she and her women have agreed to lease us some land to build a chapel of our own with some huts for accommodation. The monks here cannot accept us, either as metalworkers or scribes and illustrators. So I have told them we are off to Ireland and that is what I shall call our little community, 'Little Ireland'. Gildas forgets his Island of Witches is called by the locals 'Little Ireland' because the Irish traders settled there,' Brigid chuckled. She added that when Gildas found out where her local Ireland was he would just have to gnash his teeth, for at present she was more important to the church in Ireland than he was.

'He claims the Church owns all the land around here. Hence he can 'legally' persuade Arthur the new High King to remove the Lady of the Lake from the island. No chance. Arthur needs the tribes, we all know that. But as I said to Arianhrod, if we women are on the island with them are we not the Church too? So what goes on in Little Ireland is no concern of the men of the church.'

'Is it your Pict blood that makes you so tricky?' Merlin interjected, 'For there will be trouble.'

'And who is calling the kettle black, is it you my potbellied friend, the Trickster himself? And what trouble could that be? Possibly the confusion between my candles lit for the blessed Mary Magdalene and the eternal flame of Arianhrod. Or could it be the fact that the Lady of the Lake in monthly duty works as triple goddess of past, present and future. There are many overlays, Merlin. You know this. The flame of Avalon has been here a thousand years or more. It burns kindly or fiercely with the face of both good and bad—for without one how can we know the other, and we are servants of both. But few venture to walk on coals or have the courage to walk without light. The flame of Avalon is in the sky and circles the head of every saint or god, for the flame is of Her that is the jewel, the carnelian red.

'As for me, I am renowned as a Christian healer, a poet and a charitable worker. I was brought up by a Christian mother in a Druid household, so I know how to walk the path of compromise, Merlin. I know the superstition of the Celt, and my mother being a Pict I well know the cult of the Brigantes, the great northern tribe. I call Bride the Mary of the Gaels, so the Ladies of the Lake are my pagan counterparts.

'The truth is, Gildas wants no rival. Asceticism inevitably leads to sexual imbalance and I have more in common with Arianhrod than you may at first think.'

'You will be called a saint one day, Brigid,' Merlin laughed.

'Oh I think not Merlin, I am no miracle worker, although I shall learn some of the magic of Arianhrod, and the power she obtains from her goddess spirit. Who knows where that shall lead? I never interfere with people's beliefs and faiths, but I nurture and heal, and I demonstrate the goodness of our Lord. That is not so far from the Lady of the Lake and her ways. This was not my Druid stepfather's way or the way of the intolerant misogynist Paul. I hope I shall be remembered as kind, nothing more. However, I would like to convert Arthur to become more Christian rather than his halfway house belief as at present.'

'And in that I will oppose you,' Merlin said. 'For when he changes his banner from dragon to mother and child, his doom will hasten.'

'Death comes to us all Merlin,' she countered, 'even you.'

'Time will tell,' he answered with a smile. 'Some will be remembered, some exalted and others forgotten, but I expect you and I will live on in some way.'

'And me forgotten I suppose,' interjected Barley. 'I'm just one of the plebs.'

'I am so sorry to have ignored you, but I am sure you have picked up who I am,' said Brigid. 'You must be Barley, Merlin's student. I have heard about you from my sisters, and Arianhrod mentioned you visited the old Lady, Enid.

'So as for you, Barley, I do have the sight, and I know what you seek. She whom you saw rising from the waters is indeed my namesake the goddess Bride, champion of Britain, whom the Romans called Brigantia. This is why this charlatan brought you here.

'Presently she is served here in Avalon by the Lady Elaine of Corbenic, whom you should meet. You have already seen her at a distance. Elaine is a poetess and is good with metals—her forge flame is always alive and lit. So Bride has chosen you, my child. She is that powerful spirit which surges through the awakening earth in early spring, when the lambs are born and the grass begins to grow again for the milk cows. But enough of this chatter, for the animals need tending and my seven girls are not averse to the charms of the world.'

'I shall hope to see you again soon, Brigid,' said Merlin. 'I trust the move goes well, but I tell you, Kildare will demand you again.'

Merlin left the bothy followed by Barley.

'Didn't her head end up in a church in Portugal?' questioned Barley when they were out of earshot.

'The penance of saints, my dear, to leave bits of themselves everywhere, and sprout bones like mushrooms which come up in unexpected places.'

It was time for a supper of real food.

14

The Left-Hand Path

Elaine was a very practical person and this surprised Barley, who still had the feeling that all in the past was romantic. She had never experienced hunger or, like her grandparents, had to fight an enemy for her very life. Elaine had experienced all of these.

'You must realise by now, Barley, that Avalon is a place where the past and present merge as one. Arthur has gone now, just like the kings of the distant past. But his ideals as the Once and Future King live on. Merlin will tell you that Arthur will return. He will appear when the island way of life is tested to destruction by foreign invaders. They will try to destroy our Old Path and our separateness as islands at the end of the world, as Islands of the Mighty. For She rules here through time beyond my own, in different guises and served by many Ladies of the Lake. So Merlin says.

'Come, Barley. This Avalon is a place of regeneration. Through the cycle of the ever-living great moist Mother Earth she meets life-giving water beneath the great Sun Goddess we call Sul. Her sacred spring in Avalon is the colour of the rising and setting sun. She is the great Mother Sun, whose sacred snake, marked with her symbol, we take to our homes. There her warming hearth fire is tended by the women of the household. Fire is her symbol, and her warmth and light regenerate all life. The swift and swallow are her birds who brought us fire. The

135

legend says the swift was blackened by the heat and the swallow was sunburned in the face.'

Elaine and Barley laughed at the prospect. They talked about the nature of stories that are passed down through time until they become beliefs to satisfy most people's curiosity.

'But you cannot deny the spirit creatures, who lie beyond our sight and whose power to transform to human shape has been destroyed by the Oligarch. We women, and a few men, can lend ourselves to their power. Each place has its own Queen and Prince, the mightier gods and goddesses and the lesser ones who haunt a place.

'You have seen the Lake at night and seen the Moon god and his daughter stars reflected. As above, so below. It is her light that is reflected, for he has none of his own. He may prance like a white bull and his horns enlarge and shrink, but he can only fertilise—he cannot give birth. All seeds grow toward the light, and we are children of the Sun Mother. Yet all women who wish to conceive journey to the White Moon spring. There his power joins with them; his power to fertilise emboldens them to open to him. We here in Avalon have no need of temple and church for our place is in the greenwood and hilltop. In groves we dance and lie and couple. The stones and trunks are our altars and the starry sky above our temple vault.

'You saw yourself in my grove and pool, where you cowered at your potential, for a mirror is a strange object. The burnished disc is her symbol supported by the white bull's horns. It is Her mirror we Ladies hold, that shows yourself as others see you and yourself that you know not. A mirror requires light to reflect and to illuminate the consequences and results of your actions. So you evaluate what you have done or contemplated, not in self-admiration or condemnation, but to temper the future. When we look in the mirror we contemplate the possibility of the consequences of the future, and in trance we may glimpse the spirits' purposes to which we can lend our will. If we glance at the mirror for a fraction in full sun glare, we may see the sun dance as she does when seen in rippling water.

'Her water is as red as the rising and the setting sun. It unites with the Moon God's spring in a stream to fertilise the land and slake the thirst of moist Mother Earth. I believe you have not ventured there and that Merlin cautioned you against its pathway.'

'That's right,' Barley said. 'Merlin was quite sure I should take the right-hand path and not the left which led me to the White Spring. Yes, I felt the masculinity of the place, and a strange desire that made me so sleepy. So should I go to what I call Chalice Well, and what you call the Sun Goddess Sul's spring?'

'If Merlin warned against it then you must decide. But since you have the blood of Amazons you might ask, why not?' Elaine smiled as she said this, then continued, 'But if you go, take a white crystal stone with you and place it as a sunstone on an altar stone nearby. For there is light in those stones, as though congealed water and light, if you hold them tightly enough. You must walk sunwise around the source, and on your knees in reverence and silence.'

So it was that Barley set off early the next morning. Wenna was sworn to conceal from Merlin where she was headed. It was a dull day, and whereas she had imagined bright sunlight there was instead greyness and a chill breeze. In place of bright green leaves were the stark black outlines of branches and twigs. The grass was still green but yellowed and strawlike in places. Dead leaves underfoot were mushed and slippery, and brambles caught at her cloak, tripping her up as she walked through the dank undergrowth. She climbed upward, passing between dark green solemn yews, which reminded her of a lychgate at a church graveyard. The yew trunks twisted and turned, some touching the ground; where branches had been cut back eyes seemed to stare from the scars. Chilled by the feeling of solemnity she pressed on, hearing the sound of running water to her left until she came to the stream.

The water cut through the hillside, splashing and bubbling through or over a series of small falls and pools. The water flowed over and through yellow sandstone, staining it red and orange. She knelt to drink, as she had done at the lion's head in what seemed an age ago. It was the same taste of iron as before, not cold like the White Spring, even feeling on a cold day almost lukewarm. She cupped her hand, lifted it to her head and let the water run through her hair. She felt this to be a symbol of her submission to the Goddess—whomsoever that is, she added in her mind.

To her left on the bank opposite a crow landed and looked at her before lifting off in the breeze, cawing as it drifted away to sit in a tree further downstream. She felt that she must be near the well. She was right, for as she scrambled up the track running alongside the stream she glimpsed the well, or what appeared to be a beehive of stones built over the well site. She reached the wellhead and found it enclosed in a stone-built cone allowing the water to emerge from its dark interior. Barley walked around it comparing what she saw with what was there in the twenty-first century. Fundamentally it was the same. A covered well, a pool under cover with the same red coagulation and a drinking vessel. She had half expected a bucket and rope but there was a wooden dipping spoon. She dipped and drank.

Barley looked around at the glen overgrown with stunted trees. A cultivated orchard lay further up the hill. She could not see the Tor at all from the wellhead. Nearby lay a flat stone and, as Elaine had said, small crystals of white and ochre were scattered on the stone and about the ground, which was well-trodden. A track lead on from the wellhead to where water flowed from behind the well, making the ground soft. A small bundle of twigs lay on the stone. Someone must come here, she thought. Strips of cloth fluttered from a tree overhanging the well, its red haws shrivelled and blackened. Nothing was as she remembered.

Wenna had told her this was the time of the Little Sun, when hatefully she withholds her heat. Only after Beltane could we call her Big Sun. The place felt that way. She walked on a little way, up past the wellhead, for she glimpsed wisps of smoke rising above the trees and smelt a peat fire.

She soon came to a clearing of trampled mud and a small fire. A chestnut-red mare stood forlornly chewing at some scrub, with a thick winter coat and rough unkempt mane.

'Easy girl, and where is your master,' Barley said. The next moment a violent kick threw her painfully to the ground as the horse turned and fled uphill at a gallop. Barley was sure she heard the words blown back to her, 'I am the bright one who can outrun any man or animal— I have no master and my name is Rhiannon of the plains.' She strained to hear, but the voice was lost on the wind.

With her bruised hip swelling fast, Barley clambered to her feet. Beside the fire she saw a small man dressed mostly in dark green.

'Youm will be sore my flower, from that there magical horse, for you did not give to her ladyship proper reverence. You forgot what you were told and did not walk on your knees around her well. She is angry now, as you demeaned her womanly status, she bain't have no master. Common enough mistake amongst Christians though, for them do like their women servile. But I see you are not a Christian, for youm be having a trinket of the axe around your neck and that may save your pretty neck as the saying goes.'

Rubbing her hip, through her tears Barley swore.

'Who the hell are you?'

'I am Robin Goodfellow, an elfin person of these parts, and you my flower youm had best watch your manners. For did I not send Jack to warn you, go no further and not drink of the water. Yet you ignored him and let him fly. Do youm not think? Be your brain addled, or as Elaine told you did you not look at why you came here and the consequence. For I could do as I wish with you now that you have chosen another path away from light. The red mare has run from you leaving you here at my mercy.'

With that Robin stamped upon the smouldering peat until the fire was quite out.

'Not for nothing do they call this the blood spring, Barley, for I know your name. No, not the blood of the cycle of woman's nature, for that is governed where you first trod. Here only is the water of life energised by the sun when she chooses, but she as you know goes into the depths of darkness—and that is where you have found yourself my dear. Now come here my flower.'

Barley did as she was told. He was shorter than she expected. It was his ridiculous battered pointed hat that made him seem taller. She looked at his ears and was disappointed to see they were not pointed but normal. He stood close up to her placing his hands on her shoulders, running his hands down her back as he placed both hands firmly on her buttocks, pulling her closely into him.

'Now kiss me,' he commanded.

Barley's mind was racing but there was something compellingly awful about all this. She relaxed into him as though she were divorced from common sense, overcome by something inside her that yielded her body outside her control. She opened her lips and kissed him fully.

'Now you have received a fairy kiss and taken a step you could never have imagined,' he said stepping back. 'See, your pain has gone and there will be no bruising.' His last words came as a sigh, for he slowly misted to nothing before her eyes. Only a frog hopped in the grass and that was quite out of season.

He was gone. It was all beyond belief. The ashes were still hot, there were hoof prints, she was muddy where she had been kicked, but her bruising and pain had vanished. Yet she had enjoyed the moment with Robin—how could she? As he had said, she had taken a step beyond.

Barley went back to the wellhead and crawled on her knees like a child around the well sunwise. She felt totally foolish. But then wasn't Robin Goodfellow a knave, Puck even, or a demon—surely that was not Merlin teaching her a lesson was it? She blushed at the thought. How could she know? And that she knew would be her punishment.

On her knees Barley lifted her hands to heaven and began the charm Wenna had taught her.

'I summon from the cold clear air
From the bare branches of the trees
From worms coiling under the ground...'

She had not finished when before her eyes a smoke-like wraith rose from the water. She was grey like a living pencil and charcoal sketch, and unbelievably beautiful. Her beauty from another world—svelte, sexual and desirable yet soft and winning, powerful and full of danger, desirable like thin ice. She was dressed in a low-cut gown whose hem seemed to be of living flames or even serpents. Barley felt herself pulled to her, melting into her. She was overcome by the smell of her, that was like honey on her lips and the warmth of the sun on warm roses. Her skin was cold to the touch yet full of pulsing passion. Everything about her was contradictory and in contrast.

The Goddess, for that she obviously was, spoke. Her voice was low and sultry like a cat's purr that rolled and swayed like the sea.

'Was it not you, Barley Bright, who told the monk that at first the Maiden comes with modest face and chaste words, but beneath the concealment of the hem of her garment she is a pillar of fire? So you see what I am in you. I am that which you conceal, that is not reflected in the mirror of my day, for you see the fairest of yourself as the mirror speaks. But I say in the light you see the mirror darkly, dazzled by its brilliance, whereas in the dark mirror you find another self, and when night and day are united then peace and satisfaction comes.'

Barley fainted for a moment as the power around her became too much, like the cloying taste of too much cream and alcohol before vomiting. As she recovered, feeling wretched, she slowly composed herself and the woman offered her water from the well.

'Take, drink, for this means my essence, it is the very fertility of the earth and the power of the sun and moon as one. It is like the lifeblood. It is the eternal offering of our life poured out as libation in service beyond our selfish interest.'

Barley drank and the woman walked a few short steps to the well. Wherever her feet touched the ground a white flower sprung up as though by magic. It was all too much to take in, not rational, not scientific, not explicable. It was Avalon at last and she had arrived.

'White and red, my child. Blood and semen, the colours of this country. Long have men washed their ancestors bones white, then stained them red in hope of eternity. My sacred thorn bears the red haw and the white flower at the darkest time, when I teach men they need me, when they smell my sexuality in my tree, and fear themselves as you fear what you hide.

'I possess the knowledge of Light and Dark. You have chosen to come here when my light is not reflected by the Moon, when for these three days I am of the underworld.

'Why do you wear a veil, Barley?' the Sul asked.

'I don't know that I do,' Barley replied, touching her face and head to make sure.

Sul passed her a mirror, polished and black as the darkest night. In the pale light of the overcast clouds and the flickering grey flames Barley saw that indeed in this reflection she was veiled in grey.

'The veil is worn by all those who are not ready to face themselves, a pretext for stagnation. It hides all that we fear, that which frightens or disgusts us. For a witch or mage, the veil must be torn, the mist penetrated with full awareness of your own free will. Beyond the veil is all the occult potential of your being.

'You, a woman, can become a vessel for my energy. This is the well personifying divine feminine creative power. My water can be freely taken by any woman as the shrine of the divine power which animates all of nature. The vulva is the altar through which this divine power is at its peak. This raw energy can emanate only from a woman's body. The Ladies and the Knights all know this, and this is the Quest on which Arthur will send his men to find their union with entities and use their power to end the Wasteland and the impotence of the Fisher King. And this is why so many knights have failed to seize the grail or indeed find it.

'This was no orgiastic fertility rite, but the releasing of passion, the storm, sex, lust, life and death, and the experience of all our hidden instincts culminating in a oneness with self, nature and the beloved—whomsoever that may prove to be.'

That night Barley walked the labyrinth alone. There was no moon, just the stars. The night was cool and the air clear from the Atlantic breeze. At the summit she met Brigid standing alone looking to the heavens. The two women did not say anything, but held hands. They marvelled at what they saw. The stars were not as in the twenty-first century. There were myriads to be seen twinkling in every known colour, dancing like jewels, reaching to every horizon, some close, some far and the Milky Way hanging down like curtain drapes just beyond fingertips. The great stars of the constellations stood out as she had never seen them before. They were bright and obvious patterns for all to see to make the patterns and familiar connections. The jewel lights were white and pink and blue, and the veils a soft burgundy and aqua. You could look down as well as up and see nothing but eternal light and majesty.

Looking earthward, you could see the great lake shimmering and mirroring what was above. The Lake was alive with light, sparkling with colour in rippling wavelets to the foot of the Tor to the north. Dark patches of woodland broke the continuum of the heavens in places and the islands stood black against the pattern of jewels reflected in the water. Reed beds swayed and the stars mingled and floated, as though a wind drifted them hither and thither. It was a breathtaking, awe-inspiring sight. This was truly the temple of the stars.

'As above so below,' Brigid whispered, and so it was. Barley saw there was no need to imagine giants crafted by men, or draw lines on a map, stretching one's imagination. This land of water, of the value of the nature of women, was all at one with the cosmos, with the stars above which drew you to heaven and filled you with the power of wonder.

She felt the ground tremble beneath her feet as Gwynn ap Nudd smiled.

And so the silver wheel of the great temple turned that night.

Piran's Manuscript

S he woke under the tree in Glastonbury Abbey, the warmth of the sun making her feel dozey. Her book had slipped to the ground. Disconcertingly, the strange man was stood looking at her, but he just smiled, nodded and walked away. She slept the next day then returned home.

That was a year ago.

Another day, another town. Now she was exploring Tintagel. She had been to Arthur's Hall and seen the glorious stained glass windows. What caught her attention there was a sword and a helmet with horse-hair plumes. She had seen the like in what she now described as her nightmare, the dream that plagued her—for she felt it real and it had changed her thinking. These objects in the glass cases were real. She was certain she had seen them before.

She strolled down the street looking to find the pasty shop she had passed on her way up from the castle. Certainly, the castle was more ancient than she had realised; but not from her dreamtime. Romanticised, yes in its medieval form, but still she felt it was an ancient power point for sure. She was waiting for archaeologists one day to realise that somewhere there on the promontory lay the palace of Gorlois and Uther.

She glanced into an art shop called Another Green Place. A small friendly-looking man was at a desk painting. He had the world written into his features. His current work at his desk was of a dragon, a white dragon. Around the wall hung paintings of various styles—many of them Arthurian or 'magical'.

She stood beneath a large pentacle suspended from the ceiling. For a moment the ground seemed to shift. On the wall was a painting of a woman rising from water. It was the epitome of Sul. She wanted it so badly but it was sold.

'She is going home to Glastonbury,' the man said. 'She is the Lady of the Lake personified.'

She noticed a small booklet for sale called The Ladies of the Lake. She opened it and for a moment was again shocked, caught off-guard. Was this another dream? Here were the images that Piran had illustrated for her. For on the day she left Avalon Piran had arrived breathless and in a hurry.

'I know you liked my work, Barley,' Piran had said. 'I have painted on a series of richly-coloured icon images for you as keepsake of this place. I worked in secret from Brother Gildas. I have noted down what I learned of the women hereabouts and preserved them in colour. No one will believe we were not savages and barbarians, that we wore fine clothes and had French wine glasses and dates from Arabia and wine from Tunis or armour from Byzantium. For Merlin tells me a great plague will come with their trade, and we will succumb and become so weak the Saxons will envelop us all. Then we will become legend and myth. I believe Merlin.'

He passed into her hand a set of illuminated pictures of the Ladies of the Lake. They were beautiful, strangely ancient yet futuristic, more medieval and not of his time. Every woman was peering from a window. Piran had secretly designed these for his own purpose, but felt in his being that she should own them. Of course in time travel they had evaporated as part of what she assumed was a dream. Yet here they were laid out in her hands.

I have found my Avalon again, she breathed out silently. This seems unbelievable, yet it is true, she thought.

'We know,' a voice said.

The artist smiled.

THE
BOOK of PIRAN

BY MY HAND, Dalfinet, a troubadour, do testify that
in the year of our Lord eleven hundred and forty-seven
I discovered in a cave close by the vallee de l'Absinthe,
on the promontory of the Boulinettes, an ancient illuminated manuscript ascribed to an unnamed Breton Brother
which I believe to be the Piran of the legend of Avalon.
I have bound these manuscripts and portraits and present
them to you My Lady ELEONORE D'AQUITAINE,
Queen of our practice, for your treasure.

I hail you my QUEEN OF LOVE
For yours is the beauty of the Sun in splendour
Like the silent moon, you turn fire to silver tears
May the stars of the Queen of Heaven adorn you
May you ride the dragon and tame the leopards
Drinking the horn of plenty
Whilst throning above the many waters.

THE MANUSCRIPT

ARIANHROD OF THE SILVER WHEEL

When you cannot know yourself and as I know you, look upon me as a summary of what you could or should be, have been or could be for I am Mystery and at the centre of all effects. I rule the sisters four times three. I have no time for time is me. I look both ways past and future but only now is the moment to be seized. I cannot be changed but I change thee.

I sit serene in Glaston's bower and turn my face around my tower shedding light as I see fit. Sometimes I shelter stars within my crescent or fairies choose to sit within my circle.

As I turn the wheel, my many hues may blue or red or golden seem, but silver I really art. My light gives form to shadows and those creatures of the dark both natural and spirit. Bats may flit and fox and badger hunt by my soft light, but my gift is drawing womankind through my cycles and their season of fertility. I am the whole beauty of the turning year and seasons and the sum of the beauty of the Lake.

My beauty is best seen when I turn my face to you but my power is best felt when I am dark and shadowed. By the rising of the moon we shall meet someday in shadowland. I entreat you to taste my essence in my fragrant being, the sum of all healing waters. Smell me, taste me.

This is my final word. The circle turns but never ends, for I am She, I am the wheel, the sum of all and beloved by those of the Craft of the Wise.

MORGAN LE FAY

I am Morgan, Morganna to my friends, Queen of Fairy and Black Enchantress. I am Queen of the Northern World where the sun sinks and the gnomes live and toil for gold.

As for you and I, look into the corners of your soul and find me there, hidden, waiting for you to find me and for you to be found. Then I can empower you, complete you and offer you the silver apples of the moon for your lover to taste of your danger and inner beauty. I am the part of you which you hide, which is secret and that lays unseen to prying eyes. Perhaps even you do not wish to see me but I am here.

I heal your wounds with pain, for pain when faced and held close is relieved in body and soul. I am both love and hate. Like winter I am death, but now is the quiet time before the storms come from the seas of life, so you see I am also life in repose like a seed stored safely, like a warm cloak to ease the chill. I live and work my magic upon the hollow hills from which the waters flow, the essence and springs of life. The warm and icy waters, red and white, pour forth from the green mounds of deepest mother earth, of which the greatest of all is found in Avalon.

I dance upon the hollow hills where ancestors lie and I walk in ancient places of lost souls. Within the hollow hills ancestors lie with painted red bones. See me in my image, clothed in midnight blue as like the silent and still pool beneath the stars. Come to me in the darkness of the cavern within the long barrows where I heal and mend, transform and bring to life. I am the dark wraith of the quickening night striking fear, yet bright lady of the dawn summoning hope and bringing peace. I am the conflict of your soul, your skin longing, seeking touch from he who dares and your red lips to insure his service. My heart is as Bran's raven's feathers, dark, deep with the old craft, my hair is silver born of the Moon and frost to come. I stand where the veil is thin and candles burn for the departed. I remember. Winter comes but I am reborn in you.

Will you dare to be my lover? Come to me for peace and taste the red lips that pull you to my bosom. For I am in control, in need of no one, but I desire to fulfil my need, to possess and own, and when I am manifested in you and you yield to my desire then I will reward you with my trust and loyalty, and bring you what you imagine and want, deep within you – I will birth it.

My Place in Time:	October-November (end and beginning of the Celtic year)
My Floral Signs:	Apple, Spindleberry and Elderberry
Where to find Me:	Glastonbury Tor
Totem animal:	European Wolf
Zodiac link:	Scorpio

[all]

NIMUE, SORCERESS AND NEMESIS

Come to me my lover in the cold of evening when the hunter's moon shines a bright path to a lover's dell. I emerge from the greenwood, from the sacred pool deep in the forest green. Come reach out for me, join me in the depths of amour's embrace within the still clear waters, sink with me beneath the waters, you will feel no pain in my embrace. See how I tease you. My roving eye draws you to the excitement of the chase, my challenge to you is the shadows moving silently to trick you, deceiving with moonbeams before the arrow pierces your heart.

It is the darkest time when days are short and my night long for the wild hunt. Dare you hunt with me? Or do you the stag feel hunted, haunted by my thirst for magic and the hidden knowledge. No youth or boy for me; I crave the embrace of wisdom and aim my golden arrows true to my prey's heart. Share with me your all and thine I shall be in the dark oak groves where ancient races sacrificed and joined in sacred unity, where the sprites dwell who watch our love making with twisted faces and gay giggles.

I am the Huntress queen of the forest, wild, untamed, yet treading quietly upon the forest earthen floor amongst the creatures of the night. See how I look at you, my roving eye that you know is part of you, that challenges, that enjoys the chase, the shot, the capture and surrender. Whilst a hunters heart beats within me it is fair Roman Venus who is my tutor and whose star I am. With my silent tread and with sensing caution I choose my prey. I stalk. I aim my arrows and there is no escape or antidote, for my lips are like the honey and my breath intoxicating wine. My body moves in the rhythm of rising earth that throbs and undulates with life and living things that creep and crawl in every secret place. I hold the heart of men close to me. Choose me and I choose you, eye to eye. He is yours to claim if you have the courage to match my bold and roving eye. You are the woman but I am the spirit which drives you to those flirtations and assignations.

Adventure and excitement is my way, looking to every crevice for the 'knowing' I want. So my arrows are straight like my flirtatious words and my skill in the field preserves my freedom for I am not tameable. Do not play games with me for I will trap you before you know it and plainly tell you of your error. I flirt but mean to fulfil. Be warned.

Oh Merlin, I did entrap you but I feel still uneasy that the trap was mine, the purpose yours. You see I am intrigued and hate you for it, but is it love?

My Place in Time:	November-December
My Floral Signs:	Horse Chestnut, Mistletoe and Holly
Where to find Me:	Aller and Beer Woods, Oak and Yew tree groves
Totem animal:	The Stag in Splendour
Zodiac link:	Sagittarius

RAGNELL, THE LOATHLY LADY,
DAME OF RIDDLES

Our eyes may deceive us like the barren land where the seed is buried. I am not what I seem; I am warmed by my inner fire. You may not judge my beauty by what you see but my passion is as no other, fuelled by the need to live beyond what is seen.

My indigo gown reflects the sky at this darkest time of night. I am red and gold and green, and seen in dead leaves that lie beneath the magic of evergreen and berry bright. This is a Fay time when the Forest sleeps, when leaves have fled and branches are bleak and stark against the sky. My beauty touched by magic is hidden of earth, yet not of earth. So where do I place my power?

I ask of you a choice. To see me as you think I am, or as I am, or shall prove to be. The triple light upon my forehead marks me out as child of light. Yet darkness is at fullness. Like the husk of seed withered and dry my beauty may be. Touch me and I am of moist love that breaks the restraint of what appears to be.

The wild unicorn, which ruts stag-like and paws the ground in splendor, is the incarnation of the fearsome animal passions of raw nature latent in my season. The unicorn is my friend and settles by my side, so here lies the question of how the unknown, the marvellous, or the threatening is brought to beauty as my consort. The unicorn is no soft cuddly plaything but mature, hard to the

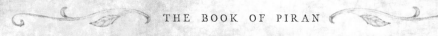

touch, trembling with passion and comforted by my hand.

Through me men see beyond the obvious as I am practical and move with prudence to achieve my ambitions with them or through them. I am no gift giver or profligate with myself; it is a question of seeking and finding me.

My Place in Time:	December-January
My Floral Signs:	Ivy, Wych Hazel and Yew
Where to find Me:	Muchelney, Fens and Waterlands
Totem animal:	Unicorn
Zodiac link:	Capricorn

DINDRAINE, GRAIL CHAMPION AND SEER,
FLOWER OF THE WASTELAND

I hold the Grail and I begin for you the journey of transformation from repose to life. I am the beginning and so prepare you for your journey of change to high fruitfulness and fulfillment of desire. I am full bodied and full breasted, strong to give to another's life. Drink deep of the Cup which overflows abundance. I am the strength of my will to provide, to give beyond my mortal means. Mine is the sacrifice which saves and brings the cup of plenty to your lips.

See me strong and bold as I cast around me the stars and heavens, a whirlwind of emotions that dominate the divine spirit of the feminine power. My jewels sparkle as I lift up the Cup of plenty which is called the Grail and of which mankind knows not the meaning. For Grail maiden I am. Might you eat of this platter or take this cup? Do you feast and drink? Yet do you not realise it is I and my sisters who are the fulfillment of your need and desire, or even lust, for we have three ages to fulfill the need you feel. Where are you my sister in this time?

I ride and sit amongst the winds of change which blow through all those born of woman. I am she that all mankind seeks in time, a return to the nurturer, the mother's womb and security. I wear the deepest Tyrian purple from Phoenicia brought here to the Lake by traders long since gone. It is the purple of supremacy, imperial, supreme, the colour of authority and influence. The Grail, whether plate or chalice, speaks of kindness and mercy. See me! I wear the Celtic Torc of gold for I am rich and shower the world with the value and nobility of my blood in sacrifice. Such is worth more than jewels and riches, my wisdom more than pearls.

As so often I have found in life that the end begets the beginning. I am the ever turning spiral, the whirlpool of waters bringing deliverance to the earth drenching it with sustenance from flood and melting ice. Now the light returns.

Come, make me smile! Giving begets giving and I love the wit and humour that oft comes with difficulties. Surely I will help you and nurture you as you grow and yield to understanding; there is oft no need to fight. Whilst I seem to look and hold my emotions close and solemn, why not be different and spontaneous once in some coming time? So drizzle may give way to unexpected sun—who knows? It is sometimes just a whim. So light a scented candle to me for light and sensuality.

My Place in Time:	January-February
My Floral Signs:	Yew, Snowdrop and Winter Aconite
Where to find Me:	Chalice Well and Sacred Springs
Totem animal:	Screech Owl
Zodiac link:	Aquarius

ELAINE OF CORBENIC

You see I am strong and raise a sword of strength which is mine own in guile rather than the steel of reality. My words bind and release like the wind that comes and goes in blustering clouds. I am free thinking and I know what I want and will use deception and seduction to obtain my ends. So it was I became mother to Galahad by virtue of my love for Lancelot which was not returned but I own him still. This is my way.

You must see me as a Grail Maiden bringing the return of life growing from the watered fertile land. In the Grail I hold, find the warmth of the sun giving the returning light, like the strong flowing love of a father which is my fulfillment. But as the moon I also bring a mother's love, a lover's heart and it is my strength which determines that the sun will come again. My sunfire has passed through earth and air and now takes form in early frost that quickly turns to water when I smile. So I am sea and pool, the tidal lake of Avalon, the ending of the rains. I now rise from the pool in which the salmon of wisdom swims. I learn and listen and think of actions yet to come.

In these still shortened moonlit nights my ash blonde hair glitters like quicksilver, with the iridescence of salmon's scales, for I am not grey but touched by the light of the moon. I may seem of elven race in the moon shimmering, floating world of Avalon and this may yet be true. In me simple love flows, and a lust for living. I know what I want and take it. This is the power of the sword I raise, it is for you to use to achieve your ends. Taking is exciting, forming is exciting, and with determination most things are achievable by work.

I can be the source to heal infatuation, madness and feelings of failure but I show the Grail fulfilling my desire through the eternal sun and this ancient sunlight. The Grail is my being held within and poured out to flow, awakening land, the body of the Mother Earth, where seed shoots within me as I bud as I did with Lancelot. My sword is my power that I can lend to you to achieve your desire. See me now and feel my presence.

I am strong but still yearn for the strength of my father King Pelles and I forever miss Lancelot, however unkind he has been. This is partly my trait, my loyalty I suppose, but also I recognize the need for the wisdom of others. Life does not always end in happiness although I would like it to be so. I will strive with my strength and wield my sword to make things happen but help me to accept loss and defeat. The sun is always warm but clouds appear and the seasons always change.

My Place in Time:	February-March
My Floral Signs:	Coltsfoot, Goat Willow and Alder
Where to find Me:	The four flows of Yeo, Tone,
	Isle and Parret, where waters meet
Totem animal:	Salmon
Zodiac link:	Pisces

KUNDRY, KEEPER OF GRAIL WISDOM, THE DARK SORCERESS

Look at me and you will see fire. Fire is in my attire and fire in my hair. See me as young and strong, able and fit, for I am potent and I am the vegetation to burst forth from bud, stalk and twig. I am the flower to come, I am the leaf to be. In me is power which is unknown to man or woman. I am drawn to the magic of life and cast spells of wonder even on those learned persons of science. In nature, I display my body as I wish and am free like the boisterous wind from the West which brings warm currents to the Western sea shore. Careless and thoughtless I seek my own ends.

In my youth, I have what many have lost—an abundance of life. But I show no pity for I am ebullient. The old may wish to be me, or lust for me but each must pay the price, for this is a boisterous uncertain time when I know best about all things. They see me budding and must make a choice of what to do, to seek my ways or let me go. I enter the dark places, and so we both may see what we did not know was there, and latent dreams crawl to your consciousness and will, I let them fruit for that is the folly of my youthful membrace.

Look up and see me drive the sun chariot across the heavens, the sun is now in splendor. With my ram's horn I summon the spirit that dwells in all things, I call the energies around me to drive upward, leaves reaching to the blue sky pushing asunder the constraints of what has gone before. I call the little creatures, the insects, all to come forth; things which eat and suck and bite which live in decay and take the life from new growth. For I have darkness in me, yet it is warm not cold. By my powers I can yet destroy, hurling wind, hail and rain to tear and dry the life from living things, bringing terror of the dark and anguish for loss.

My shape can change as I desire. I shake the bone sticks to my lover who fears what he does not know. That is why he ruts with me to prove his power, which once fulfilled leaves him weak and at my mercy. I burn bright yet show my wrath in fearful dark. I use the Grail for mine own ends, a chalice which may have unseen consequences as my Percival discovered in his quest. Dare you love me? Hold me? Caress me? Never try to tame me.

So I act on impulse, am impatient and my mood swings hither and thither. But then you can see I have courage and optimism and enthusiasm when the mood is right and my copper shining horses run through cloud. So come and follow me for I am the leader and you should follow, but beware my childlike tantrums for they can spell an unpleasant and discomforting time.

My Place in Time:	March-April
My Floral Signs:	Red Campion, Primrose and Blackthorn
Where to find Me:	The White Spring and Amongst the Rocks and sunlit Scrubland
Totem animal:	Wild Sheep and Goats
Zodiac link: Aries	

GUINEVERE, THE HIGH FLOWER QUEEN AND
WHITE ENCHANTRESS

You know me as Queen of the May. Queen of the South, from Lyonesse lost below the waves now beyond fair Cornwall's coast. I am lustrous bride of Arthur the King but lover to Lancelot, whom I stole for myself, taking him from those who truly loved him. I am desired for my fullness, beauty and artfulness in love-making. I am the Briar Rose whose thorns draw blood. My honey yellow tresses tell of the grain to come at harvest when the honey mead flows and the barley brew is made. Men have called me Venus for true, I am the star of sensual desire. I am not lithe and hard as Nimue but resemble my rival Morganna, for we are both true women, mature and desirable.

I have removed the veil and relish the blue of the sky above which I see when I look to my mirror. I am the Spring bride when the trees are decked with blossom and birds sing their tunes of mating. Yet too I am Dragon Queen and Summers Queen. Like quicksilver I change my mood and cannot determine whom to love, as I am split as if in two hearts. But in truth I love the act of mating.

The greening of the land is now abundant and I open myself to dance under the Rose of love and share my pleasure with man and beast, with all creeping things and birds. The cattle feed on sweet fresh green grass with buttercups and herbs to strengthen the bulls who seek their cows to bring to calf.

I wear the red of passion and my dove is of Aphrodite, goddess of love, not that of peace except in a moment of a lover's embrace. Earth, Water, Fire and Air is all around but as for me I am made of Flesh, soft and supple like the sweet soft moist moss and I live under the sign of Her Crescent Moon which rules my cycle.

You can depend on me to be what I am. My generosity knows few bounds hence my trials of love. For I give my favours freely to those who would my champion be. But generosity is one thing and giving gives me pleasure, but in return I want something too, mine is not freely given. For I love the riches position brings. I love the secret affairs of love. Once possessed I look for more in wealth and fine clothes and jewels and above all the fine fragrances of my time. You will not shift me from the way I am, do not confuse my stubbornness with loyalty, for I am fickle when I want to use my sexuality for gain. But you just love me don't you!

My Place in Time:	April-May
My Floral Signs:	Lady's Mantle, Lily of the Valley and Dog Rose
Where to find Me:	Meadowlands and Pastures
Totem animal:	White Cattle
My Floral Signs:	Lady's Mantle, Lily of the Valley and Dog Rose
Where to find Me:	Padstow to Cerne Abbas
Totem animal:	White Wild Cattle
Zodiac link:	Taurus

ISEULT OF IRELAND, SHE OF THE WHITE SAILS

I am the wand flame of Ireland, the flame that burns at high summer on the hills, where loving couples jump the fires of love. I burn with the passion of youth at zenith and risking all in perilous trysts and bold fearless rides upon my unbridled mare, my twin in spirit. She and I are one.

The white mare bestowing kingship raises her tail in supplication demanding union with the royal one. She is myself in truth, for we cannot be apart and are one in spirit. We ride as the wind and no man can out-distance us or beat us in the race. I drive the cattle through the fires and know that soon my youth will slide away too soon for me, but I will rise again at year's end to journey back in power.

But now as you see me or read, I am for this moment alone and care not for tomorrow and all boring plans. Life is too interesting to be confined by plans and worries. When I am tired of my sun I call for thunder, I throw a bolt or two to liven dull lives. If you want me you have to catch my attention which is often fleeting for something new is my agenda. My time is always uncertain and my roses late or blighted or just swamped or blown to petals for I am off to something else. Nothing amuses me more than hay making and farmers toil; such an adventurous time I may give them.

Heavens light is on my heels like bright flower of fire wherever I tread. I bring my light before the leaves of trees are fullest open. I paint the leaflets lightest green, sweet pink and soft yellow. My many-coloured floral carpet is dappled in their shade. I see the world in duplicate. What is red is green, up is down from another angle, and there is always another flower to be sipped.

When in serious mind I open hearts to love and tear the darkness down, as my birds sing out their love songs for a place to lay. Accept my power as did Tristram long ago when we journeyed cross the sea to reach fair Kernow where my marriage bed I shunned, for hopeless love had set its seal within my heart. Love's potion may have played a role but rash youth and beauty played its part in full, for that is me by nature. Toss aside cares and concerns and fly sweet person to my bosom. Look to the sky and see me burning, riding the pathway of the sun across the sky.

Yet healing wisdom lies in me with herb craft and the cunning knowledge that heals the wounds ad cures the poisons of our mind. See the white sails of my boat afar as I come to rescue those distressed. I am from Ireland and I have the gift of words but now is the time to sense me quietly and see me smile, enigmatically of course!

My Place in Time:	May-June
My Floral Signs:	Bluebell, Cowslip and Hawthorn
Where to find Me:	Uffington Hill and ancient chalk trackways
Totem animal:	The White Mare and Blue Butterflies
Zodiac link:	Gemini

[a39]

MORGAUSE, QUEEN OF ORKNEY

I am Queen of Orkney, where the long galleys row and my husband is Lord of the Isles; so in fact I am content. I am not a fool and have the interests of my kin at heart, I hold them close. My four sons are my delight.

Look hard at me, everyone can see I am shrewd and thoughtful, yet not cunning like my sister Morganna. Through my mother I am half-sister to great Arthur and have in my opinion more rights than a bastard to the throne. Some call me simply Anna but I am of Royal Blood and related to the King. My beauty is undoubted but I am not a fool and have the interests of my kin at heart, I hold them close. Laconic, self-assured I am Morgause, Queen of Orkney and I grasp at the Triple Crown. Ambition calls me out.

My raven locks are not crown enough so I show the red carnelian of power on my brow. The ancients called my brow stone "the setting sun." In its orange hues, they saw receptive female energies, and associated it with the fertile moon cycle of the mother goddess, Isis. My velvet gown too is of richest orange umber telling of the coloured rocks seared under hottest sun and the way I am waiting for the moment.

I work my loom to bring the strands of life to weave a pattern which binds men to me and brings me service. Each stitch becomes a dream, which in turn becomes a prophecy. When fulfilled in the hearts and minds of those who seek the way of nature, its yield of grain and gifts of fruit and mead become the way we are.

Of elven stock my eyes pierce to the heart. Men say I have the beauty of the elven race. It is true that we of true Kernow lines have piskie blood from the ancient race and hence I lay with my half-brother at midsummer in pagan custom conceiving Mordred, Arthur's true son.

Like the butterfly I fly to seek my lover outside my castle wall within the greenwood. My fearful, faithful hound can scent the stag and boar and lead me to the chase which is the thrill of dangerous pursuit. I too jump the fires at midsummer as in my youth and watch the flaming kolovrat raised high by mine own young men to celebrate the sun. But to achieve my end I move aside and like the crab claw to me what is rightfully mine own.

My Place in Time:	June-July
My Floral Signs:	St. John's Wort, Guelder Rose and Meadowsweet
Where to find Me:	Ring of Brodgar and Penwith
Totem animal:	Butterfly & Hunting Dog
Zodiac link:	Cancer

IGRAYNE, DUCHESS OF CORNWALL,

HALLOWS QUEEN

I am mother to Arthur, High King and Great Bear. I am the victim of the deceit of Merlin. I choose to wear the gold of the sun as torc, as ring, as dress to show my rank as one who is royal and no need of Merlin's whiles. I am blessed like the lion with hair as golden as his mane. The Golden Land of Kerne, the Corn Mother, is my bed and I choose whom to invite despite the whiles of the Mage.

I think myself as generous and warm hearted, especially when lazed in the sun and the scent of the rose, carnation and other sweet flowers of my garden grown to fullness in my nostrils. I birthed Arthur and loved him still despite the pain of loss and treachery for I have a strong will but I will create a drama one day through my three daughters whom I will lead to understand their roles. Drama is my way and I can roar as a woman for I am brave as any man and more so than the coward Uther, Merlin's man.

See my sun symbol, feel the warmth of my tenderness for opposites, my children. I love laughter and the touch of fine things, the smoothness of wood, softness of velvet, the sensuality of silken thread. The first fruits of harvest come easily to my hand and satisfy my thirst and hunger for the finest wines and breads.

Mine is the Golden Age to come and I birth the now and future King, the golden child but I am birth mother to many more. Now is my power time. I sit in my enchanted timeless castle and bathe in sunshine. My eyes close, but I am alert to all danger and confident in myself, my power and strength. For I have the fullness of woman and youth lusts for me. I give my experience and warmth without rancour or need for payment, just the hedonism needed to satisfy what was not gained before.

This is the time of dancing wheat, of bearded barleycorn and tall rustling oats. This is a time of stillness as the full-grown leaves of trees wait out the summer heat and blackbirds pant in summer dust. The world of Nature is pregnant and I am midwife to her all.

All the hallows are here; earth, wind, fire and water. This is my time and I have no need of Merlin.

My Place in Time:	July-August
My Floral Signs:	Meadow Saffron, Gold Broom and Heather
Where to find Me:	The garden of Tintagel castle
Totem animal:	Lion
Zodiac link:	Leo

ARGANTE, QUEEN OF AVALON AND
SWORD MAIDEN

My world is the Isle of Apples some call Glastonbury. I build another world of unseen glassy castles and a floating world beyond the human sight. I am called most often by those who do not understand the sisterhood 'the Lady of the Lake' because I stand at the doorway of two worlds of water and earth and the seen and unseen. Mine is the golden key to the very land where every leaf pauses between green and russet and so like illusive sovereignty. I empower and gave Arthur his sword and scabbard which was wasted by the arts and ambition of men. But he will come again before the end of time and the meeting of the worlds.

Mine is the time when trees yield the fruitfulness of apple, pear and hazel. Gone are the soft berries of my sister. My skirts are the green that bore the fruits of labour but my hair the colours of the harvest fields of today. My braids fall to the earth seeking moist fertile soil. Soon it will be time for the corn maiden to yield her blood to the soil for the fertility of mother Kerne. Already the Corn Dollies are made, wearing their red scarves holding the spirit for another year.

My bowl is full and overflows as the earth yields her pleasure and mankind drinks their fill of barley wine and cider which makes them drunk and addled, aware only of the heat of day. The dust of corn yellows the rising moon satiating their lust for life, proclaiming my time is here. My skirts open to the spent and weary workers with hazed lust that spends with instinct their last energy in me knowing that this quickened time is ending.

The hare leaps from harvest scythes remembering the corn maid who gave her blood to the furrow. She will stand again with the last stook bedecked in scarlet ribbon around her neck, a symbol of blood well spent. My work is regeneration, obtaining new life from old. I am all times and seasons but love the harvest moon. I love the Land so much but with that love comes responsibility which is love's nature, sting and bite. As virgin unto myself I need no man to consummate my passion and I seed what is to come because I remember what has gone before and it is my blood that flows to the furrow to bring life renewed. The knowing 'tis my way and this by intuition but also with my alliance from those around me.

My Place in Time:	August-September
My Floral Signs:	Lady's Tresses, Elecampane and Black Nightshade
Where to find Me:	Beckery fields and Cornfields
Totem animal:	White hare
Zodiac link:	Virgo

ENID, LADY OF JOY,

VIRTUOUS AND FAITHFUL

My Joy is by the waters of the ever-changing shore of Lake and Sea. My home is of the four rivers, but it is Soay that intrigues me most. I hold the golden child within me to birth at due time when the moon is at its fullest. I wear my long fair locks and think of harvest moon and yearn for the birthing of my golden child. Mine is the beauty of completeness. I am protected, loved, the hope of tomorrow.

This is the quiet time as leaves fall and green turns to russet hues, I sit by the estuary shore of Sabrinna thinking of the tides of life that wash her shore, each bringing something new. I reflect upon the sea harvest and its bounty, of the sound of the sea still carried by its shells when far away on land. From the foam of the sea sweet Venus came floating on a sea shell. Is this like me? For I would Like to live in a shell of lustrous nature only revealing myself when I desire.

I was once poor, from the isle of sheep, but as time moved on fortune smiled upon me as I married the very love of my life. The tides of life throw up all manner of strange things but I, Enid, proved my faith and constancy through all the hardships and trials which life affords. Hence as nature pauses now and vitality seems stilled but for a moment, it is time to reflect upon a life spent in happiness and how to preserve this for the future. As windblown leaves rustle in the streets and pathways, it is a time of thoughtfulness, storing, holding and appreciating what is now. For who knows what tomorrow holds. Balanced judgements must be made to provision for our future. I am the quiet one who preserves.

My Place in Time:	September-October
My Floral Signs:	Teasel, Marsh Samphire and Musk Thistle
Where to find Me:	Somerset Levels and the Severn Sea
Totem animal:	Otter
Zodiac link:	Libra

'But what of Merlin?' I   hear you ask of me before I go.

MERLIN must tell his own tales for he is an alchemist and word weaver and as Nimue doth feel, I share her doubts as to his entrapment by our whiles; but his company was pleasant to us all and he intrigued me. I fear he is close by you.

POSTSCRIPT

"It is certainly the case that a soil which has a taste of perfume will be the best soil. If we need an explanation of this it is when the ground is not turned up, just towards sunset, at a place where the ends of rainbows have come to earth, and when the soil has been drenched with rain following drought. The earth then sends out that divine breath of hers, of quite incomparable sweetness, which she has conceived from the sun."

Pliny, Natural History, Book XVII

Jan Kuśmirek

If you wish to learn more about both the science and magic of the Ladies of the Lake you can do no better than join a workshop. These are held regularly in Glastonbury, England. Information from www.ladiesofthelake.ltd and www.fragrantearthint.com

Each Lady has her signature or dedicated fragrance for personal use. Obtainable mail order from Fragrant Earth International Ltd www.fragrantearthint.com or the store Fragrant Earth, 5a The High Street, Glastonbury, Somerset, BA6 9DP, United Kingdom.

Ladies of the Lake is a Trade Mark of Jan Kuśmirek